"Oh, no, princess, you won't get rid of me that easily.

Not until we get this straightened out."

"There's nothing to straighten out—"

"You're wrong," Storm interrupted flatly. "What is it with you, Casey? Do you have so little regard for yourself that you find it impossible to believe a man could want you?"

"I'm just not interested," she snapped. "I don't want an affair or a fling, or whatever it is you have in mind!"

"That wasn't the impression I got in the car."

Casey pushed fiercely at his chest. "Well, you were wrong!"

"Was I?"

Storm drew her abruptly and easily into his arms, and Casey realized with a sinking sensation that she was fighting herself as well as him. His lips moved on hers gently, teasing. Feather-light, they traced a path from one corner of her mouth to the other, his tongue darting out to caress the sensitive inner flesh of her lips.

"No," she whispered, trying desperately to remember what she stood to lose.

"Yes," he murmured.

Dear Reader:

As the months go by, we continue to receive word from you that SECOND CHANCE AT LOVE romances are providing you with the kind of romantic entertainment you're looking for. In your letters you've voiced enthusiastic support for SECOND CHANCE AT LOVE, you've shared your thoughts on how personally meaningful the books are, and you've suggested ideas and changes for future books. Although we can't always reply to your letters as quickly as we'd like, please be assured that we appreciate your comments. Your thoughts are all-important to us!

We're glad many of you have come to associate SECOND CHANCE AT LOVE books with our butterfly trademark. We think the butterfly is a perfect symbol of the reaffirmation of life and thrilling new love that SECOND CHANCE AT LOVE heroines and heroes find together in each story. We hope you keep asking for the "butterfly books," and that, when you buy one—whether by a favorite author or a talented new writer—you're sure of a good read. You can trust all SECOND CHANCE AT LOVE books to live up to the high standards of romantic fiction you've come to expect.

So happy reading, and keep your letters coming!

With warm wishes,

Ellen Edwards

Ellen Edwards
SECOND CHANCE AT LOVE
The Berkley/Jove Publishing Group
200 Madison Avenue
New York, NY 10016

TAKEN BY STORM
KAY ROBBINS

A
SECOND CHANCE AT LOVE
BOOK

Second Chance at Love books are published by
The Berkley/Jove Publishing Group
200 Madison Avenue, New York, NY 10016

For Debi
And the long childhood afternoons
of make-believe

chapter 1

"*YOU'RE* CASEY MALLORY?"

Accustomed to the reaction—one of the penalties both of her name and of being a female petroleum geologist in a man's world—she merely stared warily at the red-headed, tawny-eyed man filling the doorway of her office, and confirmed quietly, "I'm Casey Mallory. Something I can do for you?"

Having learned the hard way to size up men quickly and accurately—in business, at least—Casey decided in that first moment that the man standing in the doorway and surveying her with unabashed masculine appreciation was going to be a definite threat to her hard-won professionalism. Tugging her white lab coat around her in an unsuccessful attempt to conceal her impressive—or so she had been told—measurements, she automatically stood, harboring a vague notion of approaching a more equal footing with this impossibly large man. In her low heels she stood exactly six feet tall.

1

Despite the imposing stature that might have cowed a lesser man, she was still being openly regarded as though she were a prize exhibit at the local slave market. Casey lifted her chin and gazed levelly at her remarkably silent visitor. "Are you going to stand there and stare at me all morning," she demanded, abandoning pleasantries, "or tell me who you are and what you're doing in this highly security-conscious building?"

"I think I'll just stand here and enjoy the view, princess," he responded outrageously, his drawling voice warm and caressing. Without waiting for her reaction to that, he went on to add casually, "Tell me something. How many men bump into doorjambs or trip over their own feet when you walk by?"

Casey folded her arms over her breasts in a defensive gesture and answered coolly, "Only the occasional uncoordinated one."

A gleam of laughter lit his golden eyes. "It must get tiresome," he commented solemnly.

She appeared to consider the matter. "Not really. A bit dangerous at times, though."

"Dangerous?" He lifted a questioning brow.

"That's right. A man at the gym last week dropped a fifty-pound weight on his foot."

"I suppose you walked by in a leotard?"

"A towel, actually. I was on my way to the sauna." It occurred to Casey that this was a ridiculous conversation to be having with an absolute stranger, but she found herself somehow enjoying it.

He looked her up and down consideringly. "Even in the lab coat," he murmured almost to himself, something in his eyes completing the sentence silently. More strongly, he added, "The last time I saw a body like that, it was in a centerfold. Believe me—I feel for the poor guy with the slippery hands."

Casey's enjoyment instantly evaporated.

"Look," she snapped angrily, "I don't know who you

are, but I wish you'd state your business and leave! I have work to do."

His steady gaze had never left her face during the outburst, and a peculiarly satisfied gleam entered his tawny eyes. "Calm down, princess," he murmured. "I was just wondering how the men around here manage to keep their minds on business."

"*They* are professionals," she pointed out with a certain smugness. "And stop calling me that!"

He laughed, a rich, deep sound that seemed to fill the room. "Sorry, honey, but you remind me of some magnificent Amazon princess."

Ignoring what was obviously meant to be a compliment, she said evenly, "My name, as I said, is Casey Mallory. You have yet to tell me yours."

"Carmichael. Storm Carmichael."

She sank into her chair a bit weakly as she gazed into the shrewd golden eyes. Oh, God—so *he* was the troubleshooter Apollo Petroleum had called in to investigate their recent problems. And she was supposed to watchdog the man! "I see."

He came into the room and dropped into the chair in front of her desk, ignoring the creak that warned of a seat designed for smaller visitors. "And you're my liaison with the company," he observed complacently.

"For the duration," she confirmed somewhat bitterly. "And why it had to be *my* section of the lab that went up in smoke—"

"Tell me about that," he interrupted in a suddenly businesslike voice.

She narrowed her eyes as she stared across the desk at him. "How do I know you're who you say you are?" she demanded suspiciously. "Because if you *are*, you should already know about the explosion."

Apparently not the least bit offended, he asked wryly, "Would I claim a name like Storm unless it was really mine?" When she didn't respond to the mild attempt at humor, he sighed and said, "I'd be glad to show you some identification, princess, but why don't you just call up the head of your department—Dr. Porter—and ask him to describe me? We've spent the past two hours talking in his office."

"Stop calling me princess!" she snapped, and she immediately reached for her phone to call the head of the research division. Two minutes later she replaced the receiver and said tersely, "Okay, Mr. Carmichael, what do you want to know?"

"A little paranoid, aren't you?" he observed shrewdly.

Casey sat back in her chair and smiled thinly, absently putting up a hand to check the heavy braid of honey-colored hair lying low on her neck. "With the trouble we've been having the past couple of months, Mr. Carmichael, I could hardly be anything else."

"Storm—please."

Ignoring the request, she went on calmly, "As for the explosion, the fire inspector believes it was an accident. And since Apollo doesn't desire bad publicity, no one here has corrected him." That didn't, she realized, come as a surprise to the big man sitting in front of her. Obviously Dr. Porter had been serious when he'd told her on the phone: "Be honest with him, Casey—I have."

"It couldn't possibly have been an accident?" the troubleshooter asked intently.

Casey shook her head. "No one was using chemicals that day, flammable or otherwise." Evenly, she went on, "I was the last one to leave the lab for lunch, and I automatically checked to make sure that nothing dangerous had been left untended. Nothing had."

"Did you lock the door?"

"No. We never do, except at night."

He was silent for a moment, the long-lashed tawny eyes watching her expressionlessly. "Who normally has access to the lab?"

"Everyone on this floor. Roughly two dozen people."

"You're fairly new here at Apollo, aren't you?" he asked musingly.

"Four months." Her voice was perfectly calm, but someone who knew her well would have caught the almost imperceptible hint of strain it it. She studied his face, as he appeared lost in thought, mentally pegging him in his mid-to-late thirties and looking it. He was not a handsome man, but quite definitely striking in a rough, aggressive sort of way. He exuded a compelling, magnetic virility. Like a Viking warrior, she thought vaguely, with tiger eyes.

"There was some trouble at the last place you worked, too, wasn't there?"

Casey gasped in spite of herself as his quiet question jerked her from her straying thoughts. Right between the eyes, for heaven's sake! Feeling tension seep into her body, she made a mental note: this man didn't pull his punches. Coolly, she related the bare facts of the story.

"Eight months ago, I was working on a government-funded research project in Virginia. We were trying to develop alternate and more efficient energy sources from petroleum. The work wasn't classified, but we were understandably concerned when we discovered that someone was systematically going through our files and reports. Security was tightened, but not before several vital bits of research came up missing. All of us were under suspicion, but especially me, because I had lived in the Middle East several years ago."

He continued to watch her with those shrewd eyes, saying merely, "You resigned."

"That's right," she confirmed without inflection. "Please note, however, that I was not asked to resign, nor did I do so until I was cleared of suspicion."

"Why did you resign?"

"Personal reasons."

A flicker of a smile hovered around his rather hard-looking mouth. "And if I asked what those reasons were?"

"I'd tell you to go to hell."

"That's what I thought." He settled back in his chair, again ignoring the warning creak. "Did they ever find the guilty party? As I remember, the whole thing was hushed up."

"Like you said—it was hushed up."

He smiled crookedly. "You're not very forthcoming with information, are you, princess?"

Having finally realized that this irritating man was going to go on calling her by that absurd name in spite of anything she might say, Casey merely acknowledged the question. "Not very, no. At the moment, I happen to be interested only in Apollo's problems."

He opened his mouth to respond to that, only to be interrupted by a cheerful voice from the open doorway.

"Casey, love, have lunch with me!"

"She's booked," Storm Carmichael said immediately, rising endlessly from his chair and turning to confront the blond young man standing in the doorway. Ham Frazier's smile wilted visibly as he stared into the golden eyes, and, though by no means a small man himself, he actually took a step backwards.

"Oh. Well, some other time then, Casey," he mumbled, backing up and turning so suddenly that he nearly ran into the doorjamb.

Watching her usual lunch date disappear in something of a dither, Casey finally recovered from her speechless state and surged to her feet, slamming her hands down on the desk so hard it hurt. "Dammit! Just where do you come off doing something like that? I will not be dictated to, Mr. Carmichael—understand that!"

He turned to look at her, stretching like a great, lazy cat, the amber eyes containing warm laughter. "Have lunch with me," he said softly. "Please."

Disarmed by the soft plea, and frustrated by her own instinctive response to it, she gritted out, "My personal time is my own." Absently, she noted that the top of her head barely reached his chin. Good heavens, he was tall!

"Shall I pull rank?" he asked casually, that gleam of laughter still in his eyes.

"Mr. Carmichael," she said very quietly, holding on to her temper with an effort, "my instructions regarding you included only business hours; I was not told to hand myself over to you on a silver platter."

In an outrageously calm tone, he said, "Well, I'll talk to Porter; maybe we can have that worked in as well."

Casey stared into the smiling golden eyes and fought back a sudden impulse to laugh. The nerve of the man! The women's movement might have shaken the confidence of some males, but it obviously hadn't dented this man's ego in the least. Adopting a sweetly mocking tone, she said, "Dr. Porter is happily married and a born matchmaker; please don't give him any ideas. He's so old-fashioned he'd never see that your intentions were less than honorable."

"Did I say they were?" Carmichael asked mildly. "For all you know, I may well have fallen in love right off the bat and be dreaming of orange blossoms and 'O Promise Me.'"

"Sure," Casey agreed dryly, "and I believe in the tooth fairy and Santa Claus."

"You have no faith in love at first sight, huh?"

"Hardly." Bitterness crept into her voice. "I'm twenty-eight, Mr. Carmichael; I've learned to tell the difference between fantasy and reality. And the reality of this situation is that you're a man on the make—and I'm not interested."

Apparently unscathed by her withering words, he continued to study her thoughtfully. "Something tells me that you've been burned."

For one unguarded moment, Casey was nearly impelled by that gentle voice to tell him just how badly she *had* been burned. But then she lowered her cool reserve over her face like a veil, and she was in control again.

But only outwardly. Inwardly, she was shaken and un-easy. Shaken because her heart had been tapping away in double time since she'd first looked up and seen him standing in her doorway; uneasy for the same reason.

This man was strangely attractive to her, and that was the last thing she needed. Her instincts were loudly clam-oring that he was both intelligent and dangerous. Would he—could he—add up certain items in her past and begin to wonder, as she herself had wondered these past weeks? But no, that was highly unlikely. What had hap-pened in Virginia had been, as he'd said, "hushed up." No one not directly connected with the project knew what had really happened.

And she hadn't lost her position there. She'd resigned completely voluntarily, exactly as she'd told Carmichael. No pressure had been brought to bear on her. It had been her own shame and disgust that had caused her to . . .

Realizing abruptly that the troubleshooter—and there was a word!—was still waiting for a response to his questioning comment, she straightened and half shrugged away the weight of her too-recent memories. "It's simply a question of self-protection, Mr. Carmichael."

"If you don't start calling me Storm," he objected mildly. "I'm going to take drastic measures."

Her feminine instincts understood the warning with no trouble at all, but her curiosity got the better of her. "And just what kind of drastic measures did you have in mind, Mr. Carmichael?" she asked, deliberately baiting.

"You're woman enough to know what kind," he re-sponded softly, the tiger eyes laughing. "In fact, I'd say you were more woman than most men would know what to do with."

"But not you?" She heard the breathlessness in her voice, knew that her face was flushed, and was irritated with herself for responding, even unconsciously, to his seductive tone.

"Not me," he agreed, something besides laughter now

darkening the golden eyes. "I'm man enough to take you on, princess. And the sooner you realize that and stop fighting me, the better it'll be for both of us."

"You've got a hell of a nerve," she managed weakly, the utter certainty of his voice literally stealing her breath. It didn't help the rapid-fire pace of her heart very much, either.

He chuckled softly. "Don't worry, honey, I won't rush you. Much. Now, shed that lab coat and let's have lunch."

A lifetime with an autocratic father had conditioned Casey to respond automatically to the voice of command—and this man had it down pat. She had slipped out of the white coat and hung it on the rack by her desk before she remembered that he was neither her father nor her boss, dammit, and what was she doing obeying him? "Now, look," she began heatedly, turning back to confront him. But she never finished the sentence, because the expression in his eyes made her forget whatever she had planned to say.

"Good Lord, woman," he muttered in an oddly choked voice, "you should be arrested for wandering around like that!"

"I'm wearing slacks!" she defended in an indignant squeak.

"Honey," he murmured, eyeing her close-fitting dark brown slacks, matching tailored vest, and long-sleeved cream blouse, "you could get arrested wearing a choir robe."

Casey stared at him for a moment and then turned silently back to the rack and reached for her blazer. How could a woman remain decently mad at a man who said things like that—and sounded as if he meant them, too? Heaven knew she'd heard all the lines. The old saying about men not making passes at six-foot lasses might well have been true in most circumstances, but it couldn't be proven by Casey.

Granted, she'd stood head and shoulders above most of the fellows in high school. But once she'd hit college—with a burning determination to follow in her father's scientific footsteps—she'd discovered quite a few men who liked women on the large side. And they had all made use of flowery phrases and eons-old flattery.

But this man... His compliments—if they could be called that—were bluntly stated, not in the least flowery, and held a disturbing ring of honesty. The look in his tiger eyes was different, too. It wasn't that calculating, time-to-make-a-conquest look. It was something deeper and... and something she didn't want to think too much about.

Casey suddenly became aware that he had stepped closer, helping her with the blazer, and she tried not to stiffen as his hands fell onto her shoulders. The next moment, though, she was whirling with a smothered exclamation when one of those hands seemed to tangle in her hair, freeing the neat braid from its confinement.

She reached for the tortoise-shell clasp he held, muttering, "Dammit. Now see what you've done! It'll take ten minutes to put it back up, and—" She halted abruptly, feeling the heavy braid unwind itself and simultaneously realizing that his action had not been accidental.

"Why do you wear it up?" he queried absently, watching the honey-colored hair fall past the flare of her hips. "It's georgeous. I knew it would be."

"It gets in my way!" she snapped, acutely aware of his nearness, and feeling, for one of the few times in her life, physically small and vulnerable.

"Nonsense. Leave it down." He dropped the clasp into his coat pocket and took her by the hand. "Let's go."

"Will you stop ordering me around?" she practically wailed, more as a matter of pride than out of any real expectation of having him listen to her. When he only laughed and pulled her toward the door, she added an irritated, "My purse!"

"You won't need it," he assured her, tugging her—there was no other word for it—out into the hall.

"There's a brush in it, and my hair—"

"You look beautiful, princess."

Abandoning that unproductive tack, she began another. "Don't pull me along like an added appendage, dammit; someone will think I'm being kidnapped!" She tried to plant her feet firmly, but ceased the useless resistance when one of the workmen came out of the lab at the end of the hall and goggled at them. Waiting until they turned the corner and were past the staring man, she hissed, "Mr. Carmichael!" And then, desperately, *"Storm!"*

"Ah!" He halted immediately and turned to look down at her with a glinting smile. "That's what I was waiting for, princess. You have only to ask—the right way—and I'll gladly do anything for you."

"Does that include releasing your death grip on my hand?" she asked coldly, staring fixedly at his loosened tie and trying to ignore the promise in his voice. "I can't feel my fingers." She blinked as the pattern of his tie sank into her brain, and she felt an astonished giggle try to push its way past her tightly clamped lips.

"Your wish is my command!" The words were old-world gallant, but his laughing voice made them come out with a peculiar, gentle mockery. He drew her hand through the crook of his arm and continued down the hall at a more sedate pace.

Her mind momentarily diverted from rebellion, Casey took her first really seeing look at her escort's clothing and fought back another giggle. Lord, but this man had a strong personality! One of the first things she normally noticed about people was the way they dressed. But when Storm Carmichael had entered her office, she'd noticed everything else: his eyes, hair, size, the honey-and-steel voice. Not his clothing.

Now she took note of the fact that he'd apparently dressed in the dark. Either that or he was color-blind. His tie had spots. *Big* spots. Big *red* spots. Which would have been fine, except that his jacket was olive green, his slacks brown, and his shirt . . . She sneaked another peek at the yellow shirt and couldn't quite stop the giggle this time.

"What's so funny, princess?"

Casey looked up at his quizzical smile and realized that he'd caught that last peek. "Nothing. It's just— *where* did you get that tie?" Belatedly she realized the personal nature of her question and wished that she could call it back. But he was laughing.

"You'll have to take me in hand, sweetheart. My sartorial sense is virtually zero."

"I'll do no such thing!" she gasped, promptly spoiling the outraged exclamation by adding amusedly, "I wish I could see the rest of your wardrobe."

"Any time," he offered immediately. "I've got most of it with me at the hotel. If you'd like—"

"No!" she said hastily. "I wouldn't like! I don't even know why I'm going to lunch with you, for heaven's sake!"

"Because I asked you," he explained gravely.

"You didn't *ask* me, you just *took* me," she countered, her earlier irritation returning as he led her past the security guard near the door and out of the building.

"I didn't take you, honey," he said cheerfully, leading her across the parking lot. "When I do that, there won't be a single doubt or question in your mind."

Casey opened and closed her mouth a couple of times and then murmured a bit wildly, "Oh, my God!" And it was hard to tell whether that was a reaction to his casual, utterly outrageous promise, or to the car he was just that moment unlocking. It was a Ferrari, fire-engine red and shrieking of luxury.

She found that she was clutching his arm, and she hastily released it as he opened the passenger door.

"Hop in, princess."

She paused long enough to give him a goaded look and then got into the car, muttering, "I wish you wouldn't call me that."

"We're progressing!" He grinned as he shut her door and went around to the driver's side. "That's the first time in at least ten minutes you've made that request."

"I didn't think you'd noticed," she said dryly, watching him wedge his large frame into the seat with practiced ease.

"Sure I noticed." He obviously took note of her awed interest in the car, and added, "Don't let the car throw you, sweetheart; it's my one luxury. I've only had it a few months, and nobody drives it but me."

There was a wealth of possessive pride in those last few words, and Casey looked at him speculatively as he started the car with a roar. "Would you let me drive it?" she asked innocently, confident that he would refuse.

"Of course," he answered immediately, his hand on the stick shift as he turned to look at her. "Would you like to drive it now? Just say the word and—"

"No, not now," she declined hastily, feeling thoroughly baffled as she watched him put the car into gear and head toward the main gate. "You don't even know what kind of driver I am," she muttered.

"I trust you, sweetheart."

"Stop calling me that," she sighed. "Princess was bad enough." She noted that the guard at the gate merely waved them by with a smile, which Storm returned, and she irritably remembered the guard inside the building, who had also grinned and waved. A few hours and Storm Carmichael already owned the place!

With her window rolled down, Casey breathed with pleasure the cool air deliciously scented with the tangy smells of an Arkansas autumn. She stared out at the gently rolling pine forests on either side of the road and wondered vaguely if she'd ever want to live anywhere else again.

Pushing the idle thought away, she glanced at Storm and asked, "Storm, where are we—"

"I love the way you say my name," he interrupted with a sidelong smile.

"It's not a name," she objected immediately, "it's an act of God. And you didn't let me finish my question. Where are we going?"

"Where's the best place to eat in El Dorado?" he asked cheerfully, ignoring the remark about his name.

"The best place wouldn't let you in," she returned caustically, vaguely determined not to be nice to him. Unfortunately, he didn't appear to notice her determination.

"Every time I hear the name of this town," he went on in the same cheerful tone, "instead of skyscrapers and industrial buildings, I expect to see horses tied to hitching posts and John Wayne riding down a dirt main street."

Casey smiled in spite of herself. "I know what you mean. When I told a friend of mine that I was moving here, she asked me if I was bringing gifts for the natives."

"And did you?" he asked with a laugh.

She shook her head. "I knew better. El Dorado may *sound* like the back of beyond, but it's a fair-sized city."

"Tell me about it," Storm said ruefully. "I had to ask directions twice before I finally found Apollo."

"And you call yourself a troubleshooter?" she mocked.

"I'm very good with other people's troubles," he told her firmly.

The statement was an unfortunate one as far as Casey was concerned, because it reminded her of just why she'd met him. Falling silent, she only dimly noticed that he was taking the highway directly into town.

How long would it take him to find out who had set fire to the lab and why? Was his apparent interest in her only a means to that end? Did he suspect her? And why did something inside her hurt to believe that?

Unconsciously, her hands knotted together in her lap, the fingers of her right hand began rubbing the ring finger of her left hand. With more perception than she'd given him credit for, Storm noticed the absentminded movement and uncannily traced it to its roots.

Softly, only barely audible above the roar of the powerful car, he said, "Porter told me that you were engaged a few months back."

Casey shot him a quick, hard look. "I didn't think he knew," was her only response.

"Your father told him, apparently."

She turned her gaze back to the road, feeling a cold finger trace its way down her spine. How much did he already know—really know? Her father couldn't have told Porter the whole story, surely. Would he have ignored her wishes just to . . . ? Casey felt bitter resentment well up inside her as she thought of the father who would neither accept nor admit that the heavy weight of his influence was no longer needed in his daughter's life.

"Casey?"

Anxious to avoid the dangerous subject he had raised, she said brightly, "There's a good restaurant."

Silently, he turned where she indicated and pulled the car into a parking space. He switched the engine off and then grabbed her wrist when she would have gotten out of the car. "Casey?"

Casey stared down at the large, powerful hand gently but firmly holding her wrist, and wondered again just how much he knew. He had a reputation for being thoroughly ruthless at his job; that much *she* knew. Was he ruthless enough to pretend an interest in her because he suspected her?

"Casey, love, were you badly hurt when your engagement ended?"

Startled by this new endearment, her eyes flew to his as she struggled to comprehend the question. "Hurt?"

"Hurt," he confirmed softly. "Were you very much in love with him?"

He tipped her chin up with his free hand, and the golden eyes probed hers with a force she found both unsettling and strangely exciting. Then, with a smile like a satisfied cat's he murmured, "No . . . you've never loved. Not that way." Storm laughed huskily. "He wasn't the right man for you, sweetheart."

Not unreasonably annoyed by the certainty in his voice, she snapped, "What makes you so sure?"

"Because I'm the right man, of course."

Before she could even gasp, she was in his arms, being held against his massive chest. The gear console prevented more intimate contact, but she was nevertheless aware of him through every pore of her body. And the feelings that washed over her in that moment were frightening in their dizzying intensity.

His mouth found hers immediately with a scorching male demand and hunger, undeniably possessive and disconcertingly expert. Shocked into immobility by the suddenness of his action, Casey instinctively allowed him to part her lips. After all, no resistance was possible . . . or desirable. As if she were someone else, she felt her fingers clutching the lapels of his coat with a will of their own.

Storm wasted no time with the normal first-kiss gentleness. They might have been lovers for years—he was that possessive.

Casey was dimly astonished to realize that her tongue had joined his in a passionate little duel. She forgot that they were in an open car at a public restaurant, forgot that he was a virtual stranger—and a dangerous one at that. His hands were beneath the unbuttoned blazer, moving over her back, spanning her small waist. And then they slid up slowly, somehow parting the buttons of her vest, and warmly cupped her breasts through the thin silk of her blouse.

She gasped when his lips left hers to feather lightly along her jawline, but she made absolutely no attempt to dislodge his probing fingers. Something strange and exciting was stirring in the pit of her belly; she had a peculiar sensation of *déjà vu,* as though she'd always known this feeling was possible but had never yet experienced it.

The fingers clutching his lapels moved up to tangle in the thickness of his copper hair as she felt his teeth tugging gently at her earlobe, and her nipples rose tautly, almost painfully, in response to the circling motion of his thumbs.

"Much as I hate to say this," he grated hoarsely into her ear, "any more, sweetheart, and we'll be arrested. Never the time and the place..."

"...and the loved one all together," Casey's mind automatically completed the quotation even as the words acted as a cold shower to her heated emotions. With a smothered oath and flaming cheeks, she hastily pushed him away, knowing that he let her, and hating the both of them for that. A stranger! A *stranger,* dammit, and she'd...

"Is there a church nearby?" he asked in a whimsical voice.

"No!" she snapped, quickly fastening her vest and stubbornly refusing to look at him.

"How about an Air Force base?"

"No. Why?" Unwillingly curious, she shot him a glance, and discovered that he was looking around with a faint frown.

"Because I distinctly heard bells. And rockets. Didn't you?"

It took her only a moment to realize what he meant

by that, and she promptly ignored the allusion. In a voice of shaking rage she spat, "Is this how you do your job, troubleshooter?"

"We're not on the clock, princess." He ran a finger down her flushed cheek, grinning cheerfully, and then got out of the car.

Casey sat in smoldering silence and watched him walk around to her side of the car. She had never felt so embarrassed in her life. Or so frightened. Because if what had just happened was an example of Storm Carmichael's troubleshooting tactics, she was going to have to find a defensive position very quickly and dig in deep.

Because it was going to be one hell of a siege.

chapter 2

BY FIVE O'CLOCK that afternoon, Casey was even more certain that she was in danger. Exactly what kind of danger she didn't want to think about. She had tried during lunch to project an aura of arctic coldness, but Storm took no more notice of her attitude than he had of her earlier demands not to be called by that ridiculous name. He had talked lightly and cheerfully throughout the meal, exhibiting the knowledge of a well-educated and traveled man, and surprising more than one laugh out of her with his droll comments about past jobs and experiences. He never once referred to Apollo's problems or Casey's past, and that made her extremely nervous.

Back at the office, he commandeered Casey's services for a tour of the entire Apollo complex, switching gears from pleasure to business with an abruptness that threw Casey off her stride yet again. His only lapse was the still-liberal use of endearments, spoken in an abstracted tone and delivered no matter who happened to be present.

Casey wore a permanent blush for most of the afternoon.

Somewhere around four-thirty, she decided wrathfully that there were probably words to describe men like Storm Carmichael. Unfortunately, the best one she'd been able to come up with was his own first name. Whenever he came near her, she felt as though she were in the eye of a hurricane, and she had the disquieting suspicion that the part of the storm still to come was going to be far worse than the part already past. The sea was quiet and still—now. But rough times were ahead, and her lifeboat was a frail thing at best.

Not exactly the thoughts of a scientist with a keen, analytical mind, but Casey had the distinct feeling that the scientist in her had somehow gotten misplaced early in the day. Not that Storm treated her with a lack of professional respect. It was just that she had a great deal of difficulty keeping her mind on a professional level and off that passionate interlude in the car.

She followed him when he inspected the burned-out lab, listening as he questioned the research assistants and the other scientists. Porter accompanied them on part of the tour, and it was he who showed the troubleshooter exactly where the fire had started. The workmen had already begun rebuilding the virtually destroyed lab, but they hadn't yet started on the section that had borne the brunt of the explosion. It was there that Casey saw Storm pick something up from the clutter on the floor and put it into his pocket.

Porter was talking to the foreman and didn't notice. Casey said nothing about it, but she wondered.

At five, she slipped away from Storm and Porter and returned to her office, hastily gathering up her things and making a determined dash for the front door. She didn't know why she was creeping all over the place like a nervous child, except that she had the odd notion that Storm meant to stick to her like glue.

And he was waiting just outside the front door.

"Hi, princess. Running away?"

"Going home." Casey gathered her dignity around her like a cloak and added, "See you tomorrow, no doubt."

He fell into step beside her as she started across the parking lot. "No doubt. By the way, you'll have to count on me for a ride home. Your car sort of vanished. You left the keys in it. Not a smart thing to do."

"That's impossible! This lot is so well protected, everyone leaves the keys in their cars. The security guards—" As the light suddenly dawned for Casey, she stopped dead in her tracks and turned to stare at Stone. In a resigned voice she said, "You stole my car."

He smiled disarmingly. "Not exactly. I just had some-one drive it home for you. The guard was extremely gracious."

"Why doesn't that surprise me?"

"You're getting used to me."

"What an awful thing to say."

He laughed and took her arm, leading her toward the Ferrari, and Casey didn't object. If she had learned any-thing today, it was that this man was deaf to arguments.

"I suppose you know where I live," she murmured once they were in the car and had left Apollo behind.

"Yep." He grinned faintly. "I read your personnel file. Rather thoroughly. So I know when your birthday is, where you went to school, what honors you took in college. I know that your father is highly respected in the field of petroleum geology, and that you lived with him in the Middle East three years ago. I also know that your security clearance is very high, so you obviously know how to keep a secret."

Casey gave him a thoughtful look but said nothing, and after a moment he went on.

"I know that you grew up all over the world, speak several languages fairly well, love music and flowers and animals. I know that you're renting a house here in El

Dorado, own an MG, and tend to drive too fast. And I know that you don't get along with your father."

The last statement, thrown haphazardly in with the rest, turned Casey's mood from faintly amused to guarded in the wink of an eye. "You didn't get that from my personnel file," she declared suspiciously.

Quietly, he murmured, "No, I didn't. That was an educated guess on my part, and you just confirmed it."

Swearing silently for having fallen so unguardedly into that trap, she tried to recover lost ground. "What do you mean, 'educated guess'? What makes you think I don't get along with my father?"

Storm didn't answer for a long moment, weaving the little car in and out of the rush-hour traffic. Then, in a pensive tone, he said slowly, "The way you tense every time I mention your father, and the bitterness I've seen in your very green eyes."

Casey stared straight ahead until the car stopped at a traffic light. "We get along just dandy," she said finally, "as long as there are a few thousand miles between us." It was the first time she'd admitted the friction between her and her father to anyone except herself, and the fact that she'd admitted it to Storm only added to her growing uneasiness.

"Where is he now?"

She blinked at the question, noticed that the car was moving again, and replied, "He's in the North Atlantic."

"Where in the North Atlantic?"

"Sorry. Classified."

"Oh." He grinned faintly. "So he's *that* kind of scientist!"

"Something like that. He's not just a petroleum geologist, you know. He's also a physicist. And energy's the thing these days."

"True. Is that why you chose your field—because energy's the thing? Or do you compete with your father?"

"I wouldn't stand a chance in any competition with my father," she said flatly.

"Oh, I don't know," he murmured. "I bet you look a damn sight better in a bathing suit."

Absurd as it sounded, it was still the right thing to say, and Casey's tension eased. Lightly, she said, "Well, you seem to know everything there is to know about me. What about yourself? Because if you think this inquisition is going to be all one-sided, you'd better think again."

"Is that what this sounds like? An inquisition? Sorry. Didn't mean it to."

"You're evading the subject."

He laughed softly. "Okay. What do you want to know?"

"I didn't say that I *wanted* to know anything. I just thought that a fair exchange would be nice. Start with the vital statistics."

"Anything the lady wants," Storm said cheerfully. "My size is self-explanatory, I believe, and needs no mention. I'm thirty-six, unmarried—"

"Ever?" she interrupted.

"Ever. I'm a Scorpio, if you happen to be interested in astrology. A Texan, if background is important."

"Thought I recognized the drawl," she murmured.

"Don't interrupt. It isn't polite. I graduated from M. I. T. after a short stint in the army, then decided that I didn't want to be tied down to a nine-to-five job. So— presto—I became a freelance troubleshooter. I'm not a geologist, by the way, but since I have the knack of picking up useful information, I am fairly well versed in the subject."

"What did you major in?"

"Electronics. With a minor in computer science. Are you going to keep interrupting me?"

"Sorry."

"So you say. Let's see, now . . . I love animals, music,

and children, have a brown thumb, and will eat anything that's put in front of me. I like lots of fresh air at night, know how to sew buttons, and was taught to pick my socks up off the floor."

"Sounds like a sales brochure," she commented dryly.

"Just say the word, lady, and I'm all yours."

"How much do you cost?" Casey asked with mock gravity, thinking it a silly game.

"Oh, not much. Just your heart, mind, body, and soul."

"Is that all?" she asked airily. "Why don't you ask for my honor and flag as well?"

He was smiling oddly. "That would be unreasonable. Well, princess? Do I have a sale?"

"Do you do windows?"

"In a pinch."

"Oh, well. What more could a woman want? Just think, I'll be the first on my block to have one."

"One what?"

"One whatever you are."

"Ouch."

"Well, you asked for it!" She laughed softly. "What do you expect after such a blatant sales pitch? Hey! Turn here. My house is the third on the left."

He turned and pulled the car into her driveway a moment later. "You really do like flowers, don't you?" he asked in amusement, eyeing the neat flower beds and decorative shrubs surrounding her small house.

"Of course. Oh, thanks for the ride." She opened the door, both surprised and relieved when he made no effort either to stop her or to get out of the car.

"Sure." He nodded toward her MG, which was parked ahead of the Ferrari in the driveway. "You'll find your keys in the glove compartment. Be ready in an hour."

"Ready?" On the point of turning away, she stared at him blankly. "Ready for what?"

"Dinner. I'll pick you up then."

Automatically, she said, "Better make it two hours; I want to take a shower." Then her own words sank in, and she glared at him. "Dammit! Why do I let you do that?"

"Do what?" He was grinning, the whiskey-colored eyes filled with amused satisfaction.

"Order me around!"

"Probably because it saves wear and tear on your nerves!" He laughed. "Be ready in two hours, honey; I'll pick you up then."

"Well, bring a selection of ties!" she shouted as the car backed out of the driveway. "Otherwise they won't let us in!"

But he only grinned, waved cheerfully, and drove away. Casey stared after him, an unwilling smile tugging at her lips. What a strange man! She started laughing suddenly as she realized that she'd thanked him for bringing her home after he'd virtually stolen her car! The man quite definitely had a presence!

"Casey! *Who* was that delightful man?"

Startled, she turned to find her neighbor, a petite brunette of about her own age, leaning over the fence separating their properties. "Debi, were you listening?" Casey demanded in mock anger.

Debi Saunders laughed. "I was weeding my flower bed and minding my own business, thank you very much! But I could hardly help overhearing. And you haven't answered my question."

Casey crossed over to the fence. "He's the troubleshooter I was telling you about. Storm Carmichael. And I think he's about to become a big problem in my life—and I do mean *big!*"

"I should have such problems," Debi said enviously.

"You!" Casey laughed. "You have a husband who adores you and a beautiful baby; what more could you want?"

"Excitement! Can I help it if I like big, strong-looking

men? Better hang onto that one, Casey; from the sound of it, you've found yourself a gem."

"Stop matchmaking, Debi."

"Somebody has to. Left to yourself, you'd stay in that stuffy lab and ignore the male half of humanity. You're going to take the plunge even if I have to push you! I can't stand single bliss."

"He's not interested in marriage, Debi," she told her friend dryly.

"So? You don't have to be married to not be single."

Casey frowned. "There's something wrong with that statement, but I'm not sure what."

"Oh, you know what I mean! The world moves in pairs, or hadn't you noticed?"

Casey's smile faded suddenly. "Yes. I know what you mean," she said in a flattened voice.

Debi's brown eyes were contrite. "Oh, Casey, I'm sorry! I didn't mean to make you remember Roger. But all men aren't cut from the same pattern, sweetie; you should know that. And you can't go on brooding about him forever!"

Remorsefully, Casey murmured, "You wouldn't even *know* about Roger if you hadn't caught me with my spirits at low ebb one morning. And I'm not brooding about him, Debi, honestly. I'm just not too anxious to try again, that's all."

"Well, your Storm—" her friend began encouragingly.

"He's not *my* Storm," Casey interrupted calmly. "The last thing I need in my life is a dominating male." Before her friend could say anything else, she added quickly, "I'd better go. See you later, Debi."

"Sure."

Casey walked toward her house, thinking vaguely that Debi's remark had been more on target than she knew. He was her storm, all right. Her hurricane. And heaven only knew what would get dislodged by the time it was all over...

Two hours later, she opened the front door to find Storm waiting on the porch. She demanded without preamble, "Are you any good with cats?"

"Usually. Why?" He stepped inside, not the least disconcerted by her abrupt manner, and watched her close the door.

"Because my cat's up in a tree in the back yard and won't come down."

"Cats can always get down from trees by themselves," he told her soothingly.

"I *know* that," she said irritably. "But I can't leave him out tonight. Pundit's made quite a few canine enemies in the neighborhood, and he knows how to climb the fence." Distractedly, she noted that Storm was wearing a tan suit and cream shirt with a tie that actually matched, but her faintly amused astonishment was short-lived. "Can you get him down?"

"Let's see." He glanced around as they headed for the back door, commenting, "Nice place."

The furnishings in the small house were modern without shouting about it, and houseplants ran rampant. Everything was uncluttered and neat, except for a scratching post, which was quite definitely ragged, in one corner.

Casey led the way out the back door and across the wooden deck, then pointed to the left of the steps at a large tree. "He's up there. Unless, of course, he sneaked away while I was answering the door."

"What did you say his name was?"

"Pundit." Casey followed him to the base of the tree and then joined him in peering up at a pair of glittering blue eyes that were glaring down at them.

"Someone lied to you," Storm said finally in an amused

tone. "That's not a cat—it's a funny-looking lion."

"He is on the large side," Casey admitted. "And I'd better warn you about something. He hates men."

"Really?" Storm cocked an eyebrow at her and then stepped to the tree and held up one hand. "Come on down, Pundit."

His voice was calm and held an unmistakable ring of authority, something Casey had never known her cat to respond to. But after a long moment of staring back into Storm's level gaze, Pundit began to pick his way delicately down the tree to the lowest branch, where he allowed Storm to pick him off.

"I don't believe it," Casey murmured in a dazed voice, looking in wide-eyed wonder at the purring Siamese in Storm's arms. "The last man who touched him is still carrying the battle scars. And the vet has to sedate him every time."

"It just takes character!" Storm grinned at her as he scratched the blissful cat under the chin.

"Mmmm. Well, bring him in." She headed back toward the house, wondering wryly why she was surprised. Rough exterior notwithstanding, Storm Carmichael was a very charming man. Who was it who had said animals and children were the best judges of character?

Inside the house, Storm released the cat and watched as he headed toward the kitchen and his food dish. Then the troubleshooter caught Casey's hand and carried it to his lips. "I didn't get a chance to tell you before," he murmured huskily, "but you look beautiful."

Her free hand almost nervously smoothing the skirt of her lime green silk dress, she responded, "Oh, thank you. You look very nice, too."

He grinned, still holding her hand. "I asked the valet at the hotel to make sure everything matched."

Fighting a sudden impulse to burst out laughing, she said seriously, "You didn't."

"Well, of course I did! Told him that I had to look

nice for a very special lady. He was only too happy to lend his assistance."

Casey didn't know whether to be amused, touched, or suspicious. Belatedly, she remembered her resolution, born in the shower not an hour before, not to get emotionally involved with this man. She just couldn't afford to let him slip beneath her guard. No matter how charming he was, he was still dangerous. He was in a position to ruin her career with only a word. Being under suspicion once could be construed a mistake; twice would be considered a habit.

Gently, she pulled her hand from his grasp and turned away. "I'd better get a sweater or something; it's getting chilly out there."

Judging from his thoughtful silence during the ride to the restaurant, Storm was aware of this new, slightly stilted atmosphere, but he said nothing about it for quite some time.

Casey didn't know whether it was deliberate or not, but Storm had chosen the restaurant well if he intended romancing. It was a small place with comfortable booths artfully secluded from one another by masses of greenery. The golden glow of decorative candles gave each booth an intimate air, and soft music provided just the right touch. If, that is, one wanted to be seduced.

Storm talked casually until they had ordered and their wine had been brought. Then, watching her toy absently with her wineglass across the table, he said quietly, "Why don't we get business out of the way first, Casey? Then we can concentrate on pleasure."

"All right." She looked at him coolly, depending on the evasion tactics she'd long practiced with her father to hide her thoughts.

"You either know or suspect exactly what's going on at Apollo," he said flatly.

The abruptness of his statement shouldn't have surprised Casey, but her eyes flew to his nonetheless. She dropped her lashes hastily to hide her eyes, staring down at the candlelight shimmering in her wine. "That's absurd."

"Is it?"

"Of course." Casey worked up a healthy dose of righteous anger and made sure her voice was riddled with it. "I'm not a criminal! There's no reason on earth that would cause me to sabotage operations at Apollo. What would I have to gain?"

"I didn't say you did it, Casey. I just said that you know something. Or suspect something."

"If that were the case, why wouldn't I tell you? You can't honestly believe that I would sit here and let you suspect me if I could clear myself, do you?"

He frowned slightly. "I don't suspect you, Casey."

She didn't believe him. Why else would he pretend such an avid interest in a woman he'd met for the first time only that day? He had to suspect her; nothing else made sense! "What would I have to gain?" she repeated stonily.

He was staring at her, still frowning. "Casey, what was your section of the lab working on just prior to the explosion?" he asked, ignoring her question.

It was her turn to frown. "Nothing unusual. Routine lab work."

"Explain it to me. And remember that I'm not a geologist."

"Well . . . we were testing soil and rock samples. Routine. One of the field people brings in samples from a site he believes to be a good prospect for oil or natural gas. We test the samples to determine whether or not it would be profitable to drill."

"What location was under consideration that day?"

Casey was silent for a moment, thinking back to the week before and trying to remember the details. "One site was somewhere here in Arkansas, I'm sure. But we were testing three different sites that day. The information would be in the main computer."

"I'll check it out." He smiled faintly. "You're not going to tell me what you suspect, are you." It wasn't a question.

"I don't suspect anything." The food arrived at that moment, and Casey, grateful for the reprieve, leaned back to allow the waiter to place her plate in front of her. She stared down at her lasagna, only dimly noticing the heavenly aroma wafting up from her favorite dish. Her mind was occupied with more pressing matters.

She couldn't tell him what she suspected—she just couldn't! The thoughts in her head made no sense even to herself. Roger had fled the country in the wake of the Virginia disaster, and surely he wasn't stupid enough or reckless enough to come back.

And even if he had...how could he be responsible for Apollo's problems? He had no "in" here, as he'd had in Virginia. No love-blind woman who'd believed in the face of all contrary evidence that the man she was engaged to was innocent. A woman who had suffered a rude awakening when her rose-colored glasses had been stripped away and she had been forced to see a man who would use a woman for his own ends, who was a thief and a traitor...

"Casey?"

She looked up to find Storm watching her intently, and she quickly picked up her fork. "Sorry. I was woolgathering."

"Can't you trust me, honey?" he asked gently.

"Trust you with what?" she asked with forced lightness.

"Your suspicions. Your fears. And you are afraid, sweetheart. Of something or someone. Whether you tell me or not, I intend to find out. I *will* find out. But I'd rather hear it from you."

Avoiding his eyes, Casey began her meal, barely tasting the delectable pasta. She didn't doubt for a moment that he meant what he said. He would do whatever it took to find out what he thought she was hiding.

And he wanted her to trust him. That was really funny. Just hysterical. Oh, trust was an easy thing to give. But once given and abused, it was like a dagger turning slowly in a vital organ. Casey was an expert in abused trust. And in pain.

She wasn't going to give this man a chance to hurt her.

They ate in silence, and, though she was aware that Storm was sending her several searching looks, Casey made no effort to start up a conversation. It wasn't until they were in the car again and heading back toward her house that she finally spoke.

"How long do you think it'll take you to find out what's going on at Apollo?" she asked quietly. It was impossible to read his expression in the dark car, but she saw him shrug.

"A few days. Or a few weeks. It depends on what I find." As he pulled the car into her driveway a few moments later, he asked softly, "Are you going to invite me in for a nightcap, princess?"

"Do I have a choice?" she asked dryly, thinking of his steamroller tendencies.

"Sure you do." His grin was a slash of white in the darkness. "You can ask me in, or I can come in uninvited."

"That's what I thought," she sighed.

"You see"—he chuckled as he came around to open her door—"you *are* getting used to me."

"Perish the thought." She accompanied him up the walk and handed over her keys silently. He unlocked the door and opened it, and she stepped past him to walk into the living room and turn on a lamp. "What would you like—" she began.

"Well—"

"—to drink," she finished firmly.

His tawny eyes were filled with laughter. "What have you got?"

Casey dropped her purse and shawl onto a chair and frowned at him. "Not very much, I'm afraid. White wine."

He appeared to consider the matter. "I'll have white wine, I think."

She smiled in spite of herself and headed for the kitchen. "Make yourself at home," she called over her shoulder.

"Thanks, I'll do that. Hey—you have a fireplace. Does it work?"

Reaching for the glasses in the cabinet, she replied, "Beats me. I haven't lived here during the winter."

"Let's try it, then."

Casey scrabbled irritably through three different drawers, silently cursing her habit of acquiring various kitchen gadgets she had absolutely no use for. Where was the corkscrew? Distractedly, she called out to Storm, "What are you going to use for wood?"

"The stuff that's here," he called back. Almost immediately, he added, "Where's the—oh, there it is."

Casey heard the muffled thump of the flue being opened just as the corkscrew emerged from behind two wire wisks and an egg separator. Pulling it from the drawer, she reached for the wine bottle. "That wood's supposed to be decorative," she informed him through the open kitchen door.

"Well, it's burns just like the functional kind."

Various snaps and pops coming from the living room indicated that the wood did indeed burn correctly. Casey struggled with the stubborn cork and wondered absently if he'd used today's paper to start the fire. Probably, since she hadn't read it yet. She pushed the rueful thought aside as the cork finally gave, and she carefully filled the two delicate glasses.

Emerging from the kitchen with the glasses, she found that he'd removed his coat and tie. She took in his comfortable position on the fluffy rug in front of the fireplace, back against the couch and legs stretched toward the fire, and asked politely, "Comfortable?"

"You told me to make myself at home."

"I did, didn't I?" She handed him a glass and would have sunk down onto the couch, but he grasped her wrist firmly and pulled her down beside him on the rug. With his arm around her shoulders and his hard chest pressed against her, she had the dizzying feeling that she had better make some kind of stand while she still could. Maneuvering for another inch of space between them and not succeeding very well, she asked defensively, "Don't you think you're moving awfully fast?"

"Not at all." He pulled her a bit closer and sipped his wine, watching her with hooded tiger eyes. "In fact, I think I've been remarkably patient. Especially since I've been wanting to make love to you since the moment I saw you."

Casey could feel her pulse speed up and her heart begin to beat uncomfortably fast, but something small and cold deep inside her thought, *Ah ha!* So he was prepared to carry on the charade. How far would he take it, she wondered. Just how far was he prepared to go in order to get his damned answers? She decided grimly to give him enough rope to hang himself.

"You made up your mind rather quickly, didn't you?" she asked lightly, sipping her wine and avoiding his eyes.

With apparent seriousness, he replied, "I'm old enough to know what I want, honey, and I knew you were it two minutes after I saw you."

"Oh?" Casey stared into her wine, watching the leaping fire through the liquid. "And just what was it about me that sparked this—uh—interest?"

"Your temper," he answered simply.

It wasn't the answer she had expected, and Casey turned her head involuntarily to look at him. "My temper?" she repeated blankly.

"Well, that clinched it. Of course, I would have had to be blind not to notice first of all that you had a face and body that Helen of Troy would have killed for. Then those lovely green eyes started shooting fire...and I was a goner."

She hastily returned her gaze to the fire, hearing a new and vastly disturbing note in his voice. He was a consummate actor, that was all, she told herself firmly. In his job, he had certainly learned to convey emotions by nuances of voice, to inspire others to trust him. That was all she heard—an actor's superb ability to convince any listener that he was what he claimed, that he spoke the truth.

And even if he did mean what he said, it didn't change anything. "Making love" was simply a euphemistic term, a smokescreen to cover up good old-fashioned lust. Next, he'd probably start talking about what a terrific relationship they could have.

"I know that you're a little off men at the moment, honey," he was saying in a soothing voice that grated on her nerves, "and I know I promised not to rush you. I just want you to know that I won't be waiting very patiently."

Casey very carefully drained her glass of its last drop of wine, fighting to keep her face under strict control. Her thoughts were running riot, and none of them made very much sense. Analytically, she had to admire his technique. He had kept her off guard and off balance since first walking into her office, and she had to assume that that had been his intention. But enough was enough!

Pulling away from him far enough to set her glass on the hearth, she asked, "Waiting for what?" And her voice was a masterpiece of casual unconcern.

"For you, princess." He sounded amused.

In that split second, Casey's control shattered. She couldn't go on playing this stupid game—she just couldn't! There was suddenly more at stake than her career. Twisting violently, she escaped from his loosened embrace, struggling to her feet and moving jerkily away to put a considerable distance between them.

"You'll wait 'til hell freezes over," she said coldly, turning to watch him rise slowly to his feet. "I'm in no mood to play games, troubleshooter, so you'd better change your tactics."

"Tactics?" He placed his glass on an end table and moved toward her, his rugged face curious, puzzled.

A consummate actor, indeed.

Ignoring his question, she went on furiously, "I don't know what information or suspicions you think I have about that damned explosion, but you're wrong!"

Casey meant to say more—a great deal more—but the change creeping over his face made her suddenly wary and not a little bit nervous. During this incredibly long day, she had seen this man wear many faces: cheerful, calmly businesslike, shrewd, teasing, passionate. Until now, she had not seen him angry. And she knew, with an instinctive realization, that he was not acting. Not now.

"You think I'm using sex as some kind of damned lure to trick you into telling me something?" he practically roared.

She took an involuntary step backwards, momentarily flinching but almost immediately regaining control over herself. "Your reputation preceded you," she told him in a very level voice. "You are a ruthless man, Storm—ruthless enough to pretend an interest in a woman if you believe she knows something."

"And that's what you think I'm doing?" he bit out. "Pretending an interest in you? What about those few minutes in the car before lunch? Was I pretending?"

Casey's lips twisted, and her eyelashes flickered with the force of an uncontrollable bitterness. "Oh, a man can pretend passion," she said acidly. "He can say all the right words and make all the right moves—and have it all planned cold-bloodedly beforehand!"

Abruptly, his hands fell to her shoulders before Casey could avoid him, and she glared up into violently disturbed golden storms that vaguely resembled eyes, wishing suddenly that she hadn't started this. She had wanted to spark a response of some kind, to see his mask of pretense shattered, but this . . . this was like seeding clouds for a little rain and getting a flood.

"I am not a liar, Casey," Storm grated with awful control. "And if it takes me the rest of my life, I'll convince you that my desire for you is very, very real."

chapter 3

SHE HAD EXPECTED a defense of some kind, but that he should continue to play his games came as a surprise. Didn't the man realize that she'd changed the rules?

"Since you've finished your drink, please leave," she requested tightly.

He gave her a little shake, gleaming eyes boring into her own. "Oh, no, princess, you won't get rid of me that easily. Not until we get this straightened out."

"There's nothing to straighten out—"

"You're wrong," he interrupted flatly. "What is it with you, Casey? Do you have so little regard for yourself that you find it impossible to believe a man could want you? Or are you just paranoid because of a guilty conscience?"

Refusing to answer his questions, she snapped, "I told you this morning: I'm just not interested! I don't want an affair or a fling, or whatever it is you have in mind!"

Coolly, he said, "That wasn't the impression I got in the car before lunch."

Casey pushed fiercely at his chest and found him as immovable as a great oak tree. "Well, you were wrong!"

"Was I?"

Casey had always considered herself a strong girl—since her father had raised her like the son he had wanted, she could hardly have been anything else—but it didn't take her three seconds to realize that in Storm Carmichael she'd met her match. No, more than her match. He drew her abruptly and easily into his arms, taking no more notice of her attempts to escape than if she were a tiny puppy fighting the leash.

And just before his lips met hers, Casey realized with a sinking sensation that she was fighting herself as well as him. Since that first embrace, hours before, she had been waiting for this, hoping for it. She had responded to a stranger in that car—an irritating, maddening, fascinating stranger—a man she had known less than an hour. And she had been quivering inside ever since that moment.

The logical, coldly analytical part of her mind voiced a stern warning now, a silent reminder that Storm played dangerous games, that she could lose much more than a career in playing by his rules. But the warning went unnoticed and unheeded. The colors of passion were blinding Casey to everything but sensation.

His lips moved on hers gently, teasing, not at all hard and angry, as she had expected. Feather-light, they traced a path from one corner of her mouth to the other, his tongue darting out to caress the sensitive inner flesh of her lips.

"No," she whispered, trying desperately to remember what she stood to lose, but her mouth was opening invitingly, treacherously, and her fingers were curling into the material of his shirt with a need beyond thought, beyond reason.

"Yes," he murmured huskily, immediately accepting the invitation of her lips by deepening the kiss in a single devastating surge of desire and need.

His hands lazily probed the length of her spine, traveling up and down in a curiously erotic message, playing her body as though it were an instrument being tuned to his touch. Casey felt cool air on her back and realized dimly that he had unzipped her dress, but it didn't seem particularly important. When he pulled the dress off her shoulders, she automatically allowed it to slip free of her arms, her fingers almost at once returning to his shirt.

But she hesitated at the first button, drawing a deep, shuddering breath when his lips released hers to move hotly down her throat, feeling a last faint flicker of sanity. What was she doing?

"Touch me, Casey," he whispered hoarsely against her throat. "Undress me." His hands dropped to her hips, pulling her lower body against his and making her all too aware of his desire. "Can't you feel how much I need you?"

The longing in his voice, combined with the pulsing desire she could feel in his body and her own drowning need, shattered the last vestige of Casey's resistance. Her fingers fumbled with the buttons of his shirt, tugged to free the garment from the waistband of his pants. She was barely aware of his shrugging it to the floor, hardly noticed when her bra rapidly followed.

Her next sensation was of floating as Storm picked her up and stepped over to lower them both to the softness of the rug in front of the fire. Not since childhood had any man picked her up as if she weighed nothing, and instead of being reminded of her own vulnerability where this man was concerned, Casey felt strangely cared for. And passion warred oddly with amusement when his heavy weight bore her down into the thick pile of the rug.

"My word!" she gasped. "How much do you weigh?"

The golden eyes gleamed down at her. "Too much for some women," he murmured, sweeping her body with a dark and hungry look. "But not you, sweetheart. My God, but you're beautiful!"

The expression in his tiger eyes sparked something primitive and very, very feminine in Casey's nature, and she wondered suddenly about her ability to arouse him further. Cautiously, she raked her nails gently down his back, feeling muscles clench beneath her touch and hearing, with a sense of power and pleasure, his deep groan.

"Witch," he muttered, his hands coming up to cup her naked breasts even as his eyes devoured them. "Siren. Do you know what you do to me? Of course you know . . . women were born knowing."

"If I'm a witch, then you're a warlock," she murmured, gasping when his thumbs found her nipples and sensuously teased them. Her legs moved restlessly until they were trapped and held by his, and she moaned when he began to drop light, tantalizing kisses over her creamy breasts.

Between the teasing little nibbles, he murmured, "Does that mean that I turn you on, princess?"

Past trying to defend the response of her body, Casey bit her lip as his tongue flicked out to probe a hardened nipple, and she gasped, "What do you want me to do—belabor the obvious?"

"I want you to admit that you want me," he whispered, one hand sliding down her hip to explore teasingly beneath the elastic band of her bikinis.

Casey dug her nails into the strong muscles of his neck, her body arching instinctively beneath his. "Oh!" Dizzily aware of just how close his hand was to the very heart of her aching desire, she would have told him anything in that moment. "I—I want you! Please . . ." Blindly, her hand found the belt of his pants, desperate to do away with that frustrating barrier.

His hand closed over hers abruptly, preventing her from unfastening his belt. For a moment, his grip was painfully tight, and his voice was more than a little ragged when he said, "Self-denial has never been my strong suit, honey, but I'll do whatever it takes to get you."

Bewildered, Casey watched him climb to his feet and reach for the discarded shirt. He'd do whatever it took to get her? But he'd *had* her! Or at least he *could* have had her. What was going on here?

"Storm? Are you—are you going?"

He tucked the shirt into his pants and reached for his coat before glancing down at her. His face tightened as he took in her nearly nude body, painted golden by the firelight, and he replied in a very determined voice, "I'm going. See you tomorrow, sweetheart."

Forgetting that she was clad only in panties, Casey sat up and stared as he headed for the door. Questions chased one another through her mind chaotically, but the only one which emerged was a stark, "But why?"

Storm halted with his hand on the doorknob, looking back at her with an expression that showed his reluctance to leave her. "Because I want you," he told her softly.

Well, now, *that* made a hell of a lot of sense! Her bewilderment must have shown clearly, because he smiled and went on quietly.

"I *want* you, princess—all of you. And when I make you mine, I want to know that you *are* mine. I want to know that you love me, and need me . . . and trust me. I want it all, Casey."

Staring blindly at the door, she realized he'd gone only when a draft of cold air chilled her bare body. A split second later, a colorful pillow from the couch hit the door with a disappointingly quiet thump. Feeling the sting of humiliated tears in her eyes, she told the empty room fiercely, "I won't cry! I'm Irish, and the Irish never cry! But I'll get even with Storm Carmichael if it's the last thing I ever do!"

Pundit entered the room at that moment, eyeing his mistress with Oriental inscrutability and a feline detachment born of the age when cats were kings. Casey glared at him, accusing bitterly, "And where were *you* when the lights went out?"

Pundit continued on to the kitchen and his food dish. It was safer in there.

Casey was perfectly calm the next morning as she wheeled her little MG into the parking lot at Apollo and left it neatly in her slot. But the sharp tapping of her heels on the sidewalk should have warned even the unwary that hers was the quiet of a volcano just prior to a massive eruption. She had spent most of the night alternately cursing herself and then Storm, along with the majority of mankind. The remainder of her sleepless night had been spent in weaving plans for getting even with Storm for his humiliating leave-taking.

His parting words she more or less discarded. The only revelent part of the whole speech, in her mind, had been the part about trust. And she trusted him about as far as she could pick him up and throw him.

No way was she going to put a weapon like that into his hands! After trust came love . . . and she was through giving love, only to have it thrown back in her face.

"Morning, Casey."

She stopped abruptly, staring at Hamilton Frazier's lean form as he stood propped against the wall near the door. "Morning, Ham. Why aren't you working?"

Brushing a strand of blond hair from his eyes, Ham grimaced wryly. "Because your troubleshooter's in the computer room."

"He's not *my* troubleshooter," Casey defended irritably. "Apollo called him in—not me."

"Whatever." Ham sighed, his pleasant face slightly distressed. "He's got my staff bending over backwards to help him, and since I felt useless, I cleared out for some air." He fell into step with Casey as she entered the building.

Casey gave him a sympathetic smile, thinking of

Storm's high-handed but peculiarly charming way with people. "He does have a certain presence," she murmured.

"I'd prefer that he had a certain absence. Outer Mongolia, maybe. Just when we were doing so well, too."

She pushed open the door of her office and went inside, her mind only half on the conversation. "Doing so well? What are you talking about, Ham?" she asked inattentively as she hung up her jacket and picked up the white lab coat.

"You and me. Us." He collapsed into her visitor's chair and stared across the desk at her. "At least I thought we were doing well. It took me two months to talk you into going out with me, but we've been seeing each other pretty steadily since then."

Shrugging into the coat, Casey gave him a thoughtful look and responded lightly, "Nothing's changed."

"Oh no?" Ham lifted an eyebrow and waited until she had seated herself behind the desk before saying flatly, "I was here yesterday, Casey—remember? Mr. Troubleshooter rolled in like a tidal wave and swept you right off your feet."

"That's not true," she objected immediately. "I'm long past the age of being swept off my feet, and I want nothing whatsoever to do with domineering men, thank you very much!"

Ham didn't look convinced. "And what about all the cute little nicknames?" he asked dryly. "Princess. Sweetheart. Honey."

Casey felt herself flush, but she kept her face expressionless. "It's just his way. Doesn't mean a thing."

"Uh huh." Ham didn't *sound* convinced either. "Well, then, how about lunch?"

"I'd love to," she accepted promptly.

He brightened. "Terrific! Is it too much to hope for tonight as well?"

"What did you have in mind?" she teased.

"I'd get my face slapped for what I have in mind!" He grinned, then went on, "Dinner and a movie?"

"Sounds great to me." Casey felt a moment's compunction at the realization that her main reason for going out with Ham was to provide an object lesson for Storm, but she pushed the thought aside. It wasn't as if she were going to marry Ham, after all. And she had to show Storm that she wasn't wearing a ring either in her nose or on her finger, and he certainly had no control over her.

Pleased, Ham was saying, "We'll decide which movie during lunch, okay? I'll meet you here about one."

"I'll be ready." She smiled, but her smile faded as a cool voice spoke from the open doorway.

"Frazier, you're needed in the computer room."

Rising immediately, Ham winked at Casey, murmured, "I'm on my way," and then strolled casually past Storm's imposing form.

Storm watched the younger man head down the hall, then turned and propped a shoulder against the doorjamb, staring across the room at Casey. "That sounded like a date," he observed calmly.

"That's what it was," she confirmed evenly.

"For lunch?"

"For lunch. And dinner. If it's any of your business.'

He smiled very slightly, the amber eyes shrewd and watchful. "It won't work, you know."

Casey stared at him, taking in the jeans and flannel shirt that made him resemble one of Apollo's field people, and kept her face impassive with an effort. "I don't know what you're talking about."

"You know. But just to clarify things, I'll put it into words. Using another man as a buffer between us won't work. And I really can't let you try, princess. You see, I'm a very possessive man. What's mine is mine."

The arrogance of his speech deprived Casey of words for a long minute. Then, coldly, she told him, "Since I don't belong to you, the problem doesn't arise, does it? And for your information, I've been seeing Ham for quite a while. I might even marry him!" she added defiantly.

"Are you sleeping with him?"

Again, Casey was wordless for a moment. "That's none of your damned business!" she snapped violently.

"Do you go crazy in his arms the way you do in mine?" he asked softly, insistently. "Does your lovely body quiver with desire when he touches you, your mouth open for his kiss?"

"Stop it!" That awful, empty ache in Casey's belly began to throb as his words brought back memories of the night before, and she hated him with a sudden, wild rage for what he was doing to her.

"I've seen you with Frazier, princess," Storm went on, ignoring her strangled command. "You're friendly, companionable. But there's no spark there. Nothing like what we have. He'd bore you to tears in a month. And you'd shock the hell out of him if you really let yourself go—if he could manage to tap that well of passion inside you."

Struggling to ignore what he was saying, Casey opened a file on the desk and pointedly began to study it. "You'd better get to work, troubleshooter. You're being paid an exorbitant fee to find out what's going on around here, and you won't earn your money standing around."

He sighed. "Fair warning, Casey: if you go out with Frazier, you'll suffer the consequences."

"Threats?" she queried lightly, her eyes still fixed on the report in front of her.

"Promises. I'll stamp Carmichael on you so thoroughly that no other man will dare to come near you."

Her mouth falling open, Casey looked up, but he was gone. She stared at the doorway for a long moment, her anger laced with sheer incredulity. He was so sure of himself, dammit! So utterly and completely certain of getting what he wanted. But why was he still insisting that he wanted her? And what exactly did that mean? An affair? He had said that he wanted her to need and love him, but he certainly didn't indicate that he returned or would return those feelings.

And, heaven knew, they weren't required for an affair. These days, it was hello, how are you, and head for the nearest bed. But Casey wasn't like that. Her rosy dreams of love had been shattered by Roger, but she was too intelligent to believe that hopping from bed to bed would cure the ache inside her.

As that thought occurred, Casey felt a chill. Because the ache inside her was not the one she had lived with all these months, not the ache of love destroyed, which Roger had left her with. This pain was a new one— hollow, empty, and yet hurting. As if something vital had been torn out by the very roots. And that could only mean . . .

Fiercely, she pushed the half-formed thought away. Ridiculous. Of course it was ridiculous.

Dazedly watching the pencil in her hand tap an irritated rhythm on the desk, she forced her mind to more important things—like how to keep Storm from interfering in her dates with Ham. She wouldn't put it past him to make some sort of scene, which would be acutely uncomfortable for all concerned.

Various plans were considered and discarded before Casey realized that she was going about this the wrong way. One step at a time—that was the ticket. And the first step was to get through the lunch date. With a distinctly feline smile, Casey picked up her phone and called Ham, casually moving their lunch date back to twelve-thirty. After hanging up, she checked her watch and then got down to work.

She used the computer terminal in her office to retrieve some information she had filed days before, and worked steadily until lunchtime. It was tiresome checking and double-checking lab results, and even more so since she was verifying an assistant's work. More than once she found herself irritably wishing that she had some control over who worked on her staff. Several of the people under her would have been happier and more productive in another department. However, her work was scientific rather than administrative, she reminded herself, and she pushed her personnel concerns aside.

She saw no more of Storm during the morning. But then, she hadn't expected to. He had issued his ultimatum. Now he would wait to see if she would give in . . . or thumb her nose at him.

Casey wondered vaguely if bullfighters felt this way. There was something exhilarating in taunting a dangerous creature.

At twelve-twenty-five, she picked up her phone again and called Dr. Porter. Reasonably sure that Storm hadn't mentioned it, she innocently told the head of the department that she was just calling to find out if Mr. Carmichael had discovered anything from the bits of wire and plastic he had picked up in the lab yesterday. Expressing surprise, Porter promised to find out, then hung up.

A moment later, as she was exchanging the lab coat for her jacket, Casey smiled when she heard Storm being paged on the public address system. That should tie him up nicely for a while, she thought with an inner chuckle.

And, of course, it did.

Ham dropped her off at the door of her building slightly more than an hour later, not stopping since he was going on to one of the other buildings. Casey made her way to her office, not at all surprised to find Storm leaning casually against the doorjamb.

"Hi," she offered breezily. "Have a nice lunch?"

"Sure," he replied dryly, a hint of laughter in his tawny eyes. "Porter was a charming companion. Not the one I had in mind, though." Softly, he added, "That was a dirty trick, princess."

With a sweet smile, Casey asked disdainfully, "So who promised to fight fair?" and went on into her office.

"That can go both ways, you know," Storm informed her, following her into the office.

Not bothering with the lab coat, Casey put her purse away and sank down behind her desk. "Oh, have you been fighting fair? Funny, I didn't notice."

"I always fight fair, honey. By my own rules, of course." He sat down in the visitor's chair with all the air of a man prepared to stay awhile.

Irritated for some reason by his amused reaction to her ploy, Casey forced herself to adopt an indifferent attitude. "One of these days, I'll have to ask you what the rules are. But for now, satisfy my curiosity. What *did* you pick up in the lab yesterday?"

Sobering, he replied, "It was an electronic timer—or what was left of one."

"You mean someone timed the explosion to happen when it did?"

He nodded. "Obviously, whoever set it up just wanted to put the lab out of commission but not hurt anyone. The timer was set for the staff's regular lunch hour. I'm betting that plastic explosives were used, but I won't know until the report comes back."

"Report?"

"I sent the timer to a friend of mine who specializes in demolition," he explained. "He'll be able to tell me what explosive was used and whether there was anything unusual about the timer. If there was anything unusual, we may have something to work with."

Casey frowned slightly. "Sounds like a long shot," she commented quietly. "Explosives are used fairly regularly in this part of the country, aren't they?"

"Between the petroleum and mining industries they are," he agreed. "But we have something else to go on as well. I discovered this morning that someone's tampered with the main computer. Every site being tested that day has been neatly cut out of the memory, and false data supplied. So either our culprit knows computers as well as explosives, or else he brought a friend."

"Or already had a friend inside to do his dirty work," Casey added in an even voice.

"Or had a friend inside," he confirmed.

Her mind whirling with disjointed thoughts, Casey stared at him and said slowly, "I have a background in computers."

"I know you do," he said calmly.

"And yet you don't suspect me?"

"Not at all."

There was a long silence, and Casey stared into his eyes, wishing that she could read the thoughts hidden behind the faint amusement. For the first time, she wondered if she should tell him what she suspected, but the words wouldn't come.

"Casey," he said very quietly, interrupting her thoughts, "don't go out with Frazier tonight."

She pushed aside one problem to deal with another. "I'll go out with anyone I want to."

"You're only doing it to spite me."

"Don't flatter yourself!" she snapped. "I happen to like Ham, and I won't stop seeing him just because you think you own me!"

"Casey—"

Cutting him off ruthlessly, she said coldly, "You're not my parent or my husband; you have absolutely no right to tell me what to do or whom to see!"

"But I plan to be your lover, sweetheart, and that gives me the right," he said simply.

Casey leaned an elbow on her desk and rested her forehead on her raised hand. It was a gesture of despair, and she found herself fighting an inner battle to keep from laughing hysterically. Oh, damn the man! Why was

she generally torn between laughter and rage whenever
he was around? Was the curious effect just another sam-
ple from his bag of tricks?

Slowly, spacing each word for maximum emphasis,
she told him, "I don't want a lover." And in case that
didn't get through to him, she added, "Haven't you ever
heard that trite but true little thing about the best-laid
plans of mice and men?" She raised her head and glared
at him.

"Oh, I've heard it." He was smiling cheerfully. "I've
always believed, though, that if a man wants something
badly enough, he should be prepared to go all out to get
it. Hell for leather, so to speak. And I do want you,
princess."

"Tell me something," she requested teasingly, trying
to treat the whole thing lightly. "Have you ever set your
mind on something, only to find out you couldn't get
it?"

"Once." Abruptly, he looked ridiculously sad. "When
I was ten, I had a terrible crush on my teacher. I was
determined to win her heart, but discretion got the better
part of valor when I saw her husband. He looked like a
bull elephant in a temper."

Casey quickly bit her lip to keep back the giggle, and
asked, "You mean you've gotten everything you ever
wanted since the age of *ten?*"

"I'm very patient, you see," he explained almost apologetically.

She took a firm grip on her amusement, reminding
herself sternly that there was nothing even remotely com-
ical about this man. And he was about as innocent as a
shark in bloody waters. Even assuming that he had no
ulterior motive and simply wanted her, he would have
to be handled carefully. Casey decided abruptly to go on
that assumption. Because if this *was* all just an elaborate
plot to find out what she knew or suspected about the

explosion, she would accomplish nothing by continually defending herself.

So. She was faced with the problem of a man—a very attractive man, she reminded herself—who wanted to become her lover. He was charming, amusing, flatteringly attentive. He was, in fact, everything she had believed Roger to be. The only difference was that this time her eyes were wide open.

"You're looking bitter, honey," Storm offered quietly.

Casey sat back in her chair and stared at him, green eyes calm. "I won't let you or anybody else run my life for me," she told him very quietly, ignoring his comment. "It took me a long time to learn to take control of my life. And I won't give that up. Not for any reason. Not for anyone."

He was silent for a long moment, his light eyes probing her shuttered expression. "Your ex-fiancé—he tried to dominate you, didn't he? That's why you're so wary."

She smiled bitterly. "He didn't have to try." She wondered vaguely if being in love made all women weak, or just her.

Storm leaned forward, his expression very serious. "Princess, I don't want to dominate you. Don't you understand that? I want you *because* your strength matches my own. I knew that two minutes after I saw you."

"And what about all your talk of rights and possession, and what's yours is yours? You don't consider that domination?"

He frowned. "No, of course not. Honey, my woman will be mine, and I'll be hers. I won't expect any more from her than I'm willing to give, and I won't accept any less."

"A partnership, in fact," she jibed lightly.

Immediately, he objected. "Oh, no! I have no intention of being half a couple, living under the same roof and yet leading two separate lives."

Casey wondered irritably why she was intrigued by his comments, then pushed the thought aside. Would it help to reason with him? Probably not, but it was worth a try. "Storm, try to understand—I don't want a relationship of any kind. It isn't anything personal; I just don't want to get involved."

It didn't help.

"Like I said, princess, I'm a patient man. I'll wait. As long as it takes. Just don't expect me to stand by and watch you date other men."

She gritted her teeth. "I'm not getting through to you, am I? You're not listening to a word I'm saying."

Before Storm could respond, one of the computer technicians stuck his head in the door with an apologetic smile. "Excuse me, Mr. Carmichael, but you wanted to be notified when we tracked down that information on the missing sites."

"You have it?" Storm asked, rising from his chair.

"Mr. Frazier does."

Storm nodded and watched the young man disappear back down the hall, then turned to give Casey a long look. "Don't go out with Frazier tonight."

"Is that an order?" she asked levelly.

"Call it a request." His smile didn't quite reach his eyes, which were unreadable. "Even patience has its limit, honey. Don't push me past mine. My red hair should tell you something."

"That you have a temper?" Casey smiled thinly. "Tell me, will you punish me if I don't come to heel?" She thought that she had carried off the light routine very well, but something in her voice must have given her away, because his eyes immediately narrowed.

In a strangely tautened voice, he told her, "You and I are going to have to have a long talk about that ex-fiancé of yours, Casey. I have a feeling that he was a first-class bastard. Did he hit you?" With scarcely a pause, he added, "You don't have to answer; I can see it in your eyes. Casey—"

"They're waiting for you in the computer room," she interrupted, with what control she could muster.

He stared at her for a long moment, then swore softly under his breath and turned on his heel to leave the room, saying flatly over his shoulder, "We have to talk, Casey—and soon."

Casey stared after him, wondering if that had been a threat or a promise. And wondering how her resistance to his commands had somehow turned into something far more personal.

She didn't see Storm again that day. At five, she left the office, determined to go out with Ham no matter what. Somewhat to her surprise, nothing occurred to prevent the date. Ham picked her up on time, cheerful as always and obviously intent only on having a good time.

They had dinner and went to a movie, and Casey didn't realize until Ham drove her home that her distraction had not quite escaped notice. Pulling his car into her driveway, Ham made no effort to either turn off the car or get out. Turning to half face her, his valiant grin was evident even in the darkness.

"Well, I'd say that the three of us had a pretty good time, wouldn't you?"

"Three of us?" she asked blankly.

"Uh huh. You, me . . . and Carmichael. I've been aware of his ghost all evening."

Casey felt herself flush, wanting to deny his disheartened accusation but knowing that the denial would be a lie. "I'm sorry, Ham."

He sighed. "Never mind. I've known for quite a while that I wasn't making a dent in those walls of yours. Maybe he'll tell me his secret some day."

"His secret," she retorted, "is sheer irritation!"

"Sure," he scoffed lightly. "That's why he's been on your mind all evening."

Refusing to discuss it, Casey opened her door and said calmly, "I'll see you on Monday."

"Good night, Casey."

She watched his car drive away, then went up the walk to her front door. Ham was wrong, she thought vaguely. Storm hadn't been on her mind. Not really. She was tired, that was all. Opening her front door, she went inside and started to turn off the porch light.

That was when she realized that the lamp she had left burning in the living room was no longer on. Frowning, she flipped on the overhead light.

The living room was a shambles.

chapter 4

AFTER THE INITIAL moment of horror, Casey's first thought was of her cat. "Pundit? Pundit, where are you?" she called, dropping her purse on a chair and stepping over two pillows and an overturned plant. Her cat dashed down the hall at that moment, eyes wild and a growl rumbling from deep in his throat.

As he leaped she caught him in her arms, realizing two things simultaneously. The first was that her cat had tangled with something or someone, evidenced by his wild-eyed state and a nick on one ear, which was bleeding slightly. Her second realization was that the intruder could very well still be in the house.

Conditioned reflex took over in that moment, and, still holding her growling cat, Casey stepped over to the small Oriental table by the hall and reached for the top drawer. Inches from the handle, she hesitated, muttering, "Fingerprints," and cautiously used a fold of her skirt to open the drawer. Her revolver—a present from her father ten years before—lay on top of a stack of magazines, apparently untouched.

She hesitated again, then muttered, "The hell with fingerprints," and picked up the gun firmly. Gun in one hand and cat in the other, she started through the house—determinedly, but not without a certain amount of trepidation—turning on lights as she went and searching thoroughly.

Ten minutes later, the house was lit from one end to the other, and Casey was convinced that the intruder was gone. Common sense told her that a common housebreaker wouldn't have torn the covers off her bed or pulled her books off their shelves, and she had a sinking feeling that this night's work had something to do with Apollo's problems. As well as she could without touching anything, she tried to establish if anything had been stolen. The fact that nothing appeared to be missing only confirmed her suspicions. The intruder, then, had been looking for something. But what?

Trying to decide whether or not to call the police, she located a bottle of peroxide and cleaned the cut on Pundit's ear. She had just started toward the phone—once more holding both cat and gun—when there was a loud knock at her front door.

After a panicky moment, she murmured, "Don't be ridiculous, burglars don't knock . . . do they?"

The door rattled again. "Casey?"

The feeling of relief that swept over Casey as she recognized Storm's voice caused her knees to go weak, and she leaned against a chair for a moment before hurrying to the door.

"Why's the house lit up—" he began as soon as the door was flung open, then broke off abruptly as he took in her pale features, the disturbed cat, and the gun. "What the hell?" He glanced over her shoulder at the shambles in the room behind her, stepping inside immediately and catching her in his arms. "Honey, are you all right?"

Prudently holding the gun aside, Casey said into the flannel of his shirt, "Yes, I'm fine. But I've lost three houseplants, dammit."

Storm tipped her chin up to examine her features narrowly, then smiled. "For a minute there," he remarked, "I thought you were going to fall apart on me. But you're perfectly calm, aren't you?"

"Reasonably calm," she corrected, moving away to place her gun on the table and set her cat on the floor.

"Have you called the police?"

"I was just about to."

Storm closed the front door and came into the room. "I'll do it. Where's the phone?"

Casey pointed silently and then stared down at her feet, where one of her favorite plants lay, uprooted and already beginning to brown around the edges. "So destructive," she murmured. "And so useless. What could be hidden in a plant?"

The question was more or less addressed to herself, but Storm, having just hung up the phone, heard it. He came to stand before her, the shrewd golden eyes questioning. "You think he was looking for something?"

"Don't you?" Casey stared up at him. "I've checked, Storm; there's nothing missing. I haven't been robbed. Whoever broke in here was looking for something. And he wanted whatever it is badly enough to tear the place apart."

Storm didn't seem surprised by her deductions. "You're probably right," he agreed, adding, "the timer, most likely."

"But *I* don't have it!"

"He couldn't know that, though, could he? And even if he knows that I've got it, I was over here last night, remember." He sighed. "One thing's for sure: you're not staying here alone. Not after tonight."

"Now, wait a minute," she began, profoundly mistrusting the gleam that had appeared in the tawny eyes.

"We'll discuss it later," he promised soothingly.

"We'll discuss it now! Storm—"

"Are you sure nothing's missing?" he interrupted innocently. "Maybe you'd better check again. The police'll want to know."

"Storm—"

"Jewelry? Family silver?"

"My family preferred stainless steel, and I've never been fond of jewelry! Will you—"

"Stamp collections or the like? Grandmother's savings in a sock?"

Casey all but stamped her foot in frustration, even while fighting back an inappropriate attack of the giggles. "My grandmother kept her savings in a bank, and Dad sold his stamp collection when I was two! Stop this, and—"

"Old love letters?" Before she could respond to that, he added calmly, "If you have any of those, by the way, better chuck 'em into the fire. I have a short fuse."

With great dignity—and veering away somewhat from the original point of the conversation—Casey said, "Please don't expect me to believe that you'd get upset about every little boy who carried my books to school, because I won't! Believe you, I mean."

He looked wounded. "I begrudge even thoughtless little boys the pleasure of your company in the past. I was, however, referring to impassioned letters from older gentlemen. Have any?"

Casey placed her hands on her hips and glared at him. "If I do, they're none of your business! And stop changing the subject!"

The radiant eyes teased her gently. "Who, me? Perish the very thought. And those love letters—"

"Never *mind* the love letters! Storm, you're not staying here tonight. And I mean it!"

Ignoring most of her statement, he said cheerfully, "Well, I'll forget the love letters for now. Let's get back to your other missing treasures."

"I don't have any missing treasures!"

"No need to shout, princess."

Casey opened her mouth to let him know what shouting really was, but the sound of the doorbell cut her off. The police had arrived.

"Saved by the bell," Storm muttered, turning away to head for the door.

Subsiding onto the arm of the couch, Casey mentally counted to ten and then promptly spoiled the calming effect by wondering wrathfully why she let him get away with being so damned arrogant. He was *not* staying the night. No way!

It was more than an hour later when the two of them were alone again, and Casey picked up where they had left off. "I'll be all right here alone," she announced as Storm came back into the living room after escorting the last policeman to the door. "I'm not afraid, and I'm perfectly capable of taking care of myself!"

Disarming her immediately, he said softly, "I know you are, sweetheart, but humor me. Your visitor might decide to come back and try again; I wouldn't sleep a wink knowing you were here alone."

"Look, I don't want—" she began desperately, but she was interrupted by his cheerful voice.

"I can just bunk down here on your couch for the night. Do you have an extra pillow, honey?"

Casey sat down on the arm of a chair and stared at him. In a resigned voice, she said, "You're taking advantage of this situation. You realize that, don't you?"

"Of course." He smiled at her. "But please note that I haven't said a word—yet—about the fact that you went out with Frazier tonight after I asked you not to. I think we can tackle that subject tomorrow, after you've recovered from your unexpected visitor."

"That's big of you," she said sardonically.

"The pillow, honey."

Short of physically evicting him—a feat beyond her abilities—there wasn't much that Casey could do. And, though she admitted it only to herself, she *did* feel uneasy about staying here alone. Accustomed to carrying her own burdens, she was more than a little surprised to discover a certain relief in allowing someone else to assume a little responsibility for her. And she had no doubt that Storm was doing just that.

Sighing, she murmured, "I should clean up in here; the place is a disaster area."

He crossed the space between them, taking her hand and drawing her to her feet. "What you should do is go to bed, sweetheart; you look exhausted. I'll straighten up in here." He tipped her chin up and lightly kissed her, then turned her toward the hallway and gave her a little push and a swat on the behind.

Other than throwing him an indignant look, Casey made no protest. She headed for her bedroom, muttering to herself about steamrollers and troubleshooters, located an extra pillow and blanket, and carried them back to the living room. "Here," she said, dumping them onto the couch.

"Thanks. You go on to bed now, honey." He was already busy righting her bookshelf.

It had been a long day. Casey was tired, a little unnerved, and slightly resentful about the way her life had literally been turned upside down since this man had entered it only the day before. "Stop treating me like a child!" she snapped.

He straightened and regarded her with a glint of warning in his eyes. In a husky voice, he told her, "Princess, I'm fully and completely aware of the fact that you're a woman. That's something I'm trying very hard not to think about right now. Because if I *do* think about it . . . you won't be sleeping alone."

It came to her then, with a devastating clarity, that she would have liked nothing better than for him to sweep aside whatever protests she might manage to make and carry her off to bed. She could feel a fluttering in her belly at the thought, and heat rushed through her body. And it was scary as hell.

As she stared at him, Casey realized that she had somehow given herself away. Either that or Storm had read her thoughts with uncanny accuracy. Those incredible tawny eyes darkened; tension flowed visibly into his large, muscular frame.

Very softly, he said, "Go to bed, Casey—before I forget myself and give in to the desire that's been eating at me since I walked into your office yesterday."

For a moment, Casey was tempted almost beyond bearing. He was so blunt about his desire that he made it almost impossible for her to ignore the need coursing through her own body. Finally, winning—or perhaps losing—the inner battle, she turned away silently. But she paused at the hallway, knowing that the question had to be asked. "Storm?"

"What is it, honey?"

She didn't look at him. "Why?"

He didn't pretend to misunderstand the question. "Why am I sending you off to bed alone? Because you're tired, honey. You're tired and probably a little scared. When I come to you, I want to know that it's because you know your own mind."

So. She had her answer. "Good night," she whispered.

"Good night, sweetheart."

Casey went on to her room, automatically going through the routine of getting ready for bed. She went into the bathroom first, washing away her makeup and brushing her teeth, then went back down the hall to her bedroom, hearing Storm talking softly to Pundit in the living room and thinking, *he talks to animals just the way I do*. Unconsciously choosing her prettiest nightgown, she changed and then crawled between the dark green sheets.

She had left her door open just a bit, expecting her cat to come in and take his accustomed place at the foot of her bed. But the cat apparently preferred sharing the couch with Storm. Half irritably, half humorously, she thought, he's bewitched . . . just like me . . . . It was her last coherent thought before sleep claimed her.

Her sleep was surprisingly deep and dreamless. It was, in fact, the best night's sleep she'd had in many months. The peace was rudely shattered, however, when her alarm clock went off shrilly at 8:00 A.M.

Only partially awake, Casey rolled over in bed with her eyes still tightly shut and groped for the clock, knocking it off the nightstand as usual, and then half falling out of bed to find the thing.

"Do you always start out the day on your head?" inquired an interested voice from the doorway.

Righting herself with some difficulty and clutching the now-silent clock, Casey unglued her eyes and stared at the man smiling whimsically at her from the foot of the bed. "Always. It gets the blood circulating." She peered at the clock in her hand and then fell back against her pillows with a moan. "Oh, no! It's barely the crack of dawn . . . and Saturday, too."

"Obviously," he observed knowledgeably, "you are one of those people who would much prefer the day to begin later."

"And you," she retorted, her voice still thick with sleep, "are one of those people who display an ungodly amount of cheerfulness in the morning." Her nose twitched suddenly as she caught the delightful aroma of freshly brewed coffee.

"I've fixed some coffee," he said in an amused tone. "And now, with your permission, ma'am, I plan to take a shower."

Casey stared at him for a blank moment, then waved the clock in the vague direction of the bathroom. "Oh. Sure. Help yourself."

He grinned, "You really aren't with it first thing in the morning, are you, princess?"

"I am a night person," she announced, her dignity not in the least marred by the nightgown straps falling off her shoulders, the clock in one hand, or the sleep-mussed hair.

Storm approached the side of the bed, bending over to place one hand on either side of her shoulders. "Well, you look terrific," he said huskily. "Beautiful, in fact. Has anyone ever told you, honey, that you have a lovely sort of radiance about you when you first wake up? Even with no makeup and uncombed hair."

Coming awake with a vengeance, Casey stared up at him, suddenly aware of the mat of curling red-gold hair on his chest, left bare by the unbuttoned shirt, and of his morning stubble of beard. "Um . . . no. No one's ever told me that," she murmured, still clutching that damned clock.

"I'm telling you now." He lightly kissed the tip of her nose. "And I'll tell you something else: I'm going to love waking up beside you every morning. It's an experience I'll treasure all the mornings of our lives."

As he straightened, Casey fought to make sense of his words and the quivering in her belly. What was he doing to her, for God's sake? Swallowing hard, she muttered, "There are extra towels in the linen closet just outside the bathroom."

"Thanks, honey. Go back to sleep if you like."

Casey watched him leave the room, her eyes wide, feeling very much awake. The events of the night before crashed in on her, and she knew a momentary impulse to pull the covers over her head and just hope all the disturbing problems in her life—one of which was in her shower at that very moment—would vanish.

Abandoning the wistful thought, she dropped the clock onto the bed and threw back the covers. Like it or not, problems had to be faced. Even if they were well over six feet tall and took advantage of sleepy women by saying outrageously sweet things that sounded sincere first thing in the morning. And why did she have this awful urge to believe what he said?

She sat there on the edge of her bed for a long time, vacantly listening to the sound of the shower as she realized for the first time that she hadn't felt the least bit of embarrassment at waking up and finding Storm in her bedroom. Her *bed;* now, that would probably be totally different. To wake up in bed with Storm, caught in his arms, the red-gold hair on his chest teasing her breasts . . .

With a soft moan, Casey pushed the mental image away, rising to her feet and moving toward the door. She headed for the kitchen, halfway there before she realized that her feet were bare and she wasn't wearing a robe. She hesitated, biting her lip as she glanced down at the sheer, emerald-green silk gown, which just happened to be the sexiest thing she owned. Then, squaring her shoulders, she continued on toward the kitchen. It wasn't that she was trying to entice Storm, she reasoned, it was just that her robe was hanging on the back of the bathroom door. And she could never find her slippers anyway.

The doorbell halted her just beyond the hall, and Casey frowned as she detoured to answer the summons. Who would be visiting this time of the morning? The police, with more questions? Debi often came over to visit on Saturdays, but never this early, and she never rang the bell. So who could it be?

It was Dr. Porter.

Concealing as much of herself as possible behind the partially opened door, Casey stared blankly at her department head. "Dr. Porter, I—"

"I'm sorry to disturb you so early in the morning, Casey, but I received a visit myself this morning—from the police. What's this about someone breaking into your house last night?" The middle-aged man was obviously disturbed. "And why do the police believe it's somehow connected to the explosion in the lab?"

"Uh..." Casey's mind was tumbling, a part of her consciousness painfully aware that the shower had stopped and another part aware of her state of undress. "Could—could we talk about this later, Dr. Porter? I just got out of bed, and—"

He frowned. "I'd rather talk about it now, Casey, if you wouldn't mind. I tried to call Carmichael at his hotel, but the desk said he'd been gone all night."

Casey gratefully noticed that at least the Ferrari was parked out of sight in her driveway. Oddly unable to think properly, she stepped back numbly and murmured, "Come in. I—I'll get a robe." As Porter stepped over the threshold, she had another panicky moment, but a swift glance at the living room showed her that Storm had neatly removed all traces of his night on the couch. Now if only he'd stay in the bathroom...

It was not her day for miracles.

"Honey, where's your razor?"

Storm followed his damning question down the hall, emerging into the living room still wearing his morning stubble of beard, a smile... and a towel. It was her largest bath towel, and it covered him decently only by the most liberal standards.

Casey closed the door by leaning against it weakly, noting her visitor's shocked, disapproving expression in a detached manner. He was, as she'd told Storm, very old-fashioned. There goes my reputation, she thought vaguely, shot all to hell. She couldn't help but wonder if Storm would lose his cool this time.

He didn't.

"Dr. Porter." He came toward them, casual, cheerful, detaching Casey from the door and pulling her into a possessive one-armed embrace. "You can be the first to congratulate us; Casey and I are getting married."

Porter's disapproval vanished, to be replaced by an

expression of pleased surprise. "Really? Well, that was fast work, Carmichael!"

Casey was not easily intimidated. Nor was she easily embarrassed. And she'd usually been able to deal with a crisis. But for the life of her, she couldn't find words to explain this situation.

Here she stood, face to face with an old friend of her father's—who would no doubt find some way of contacting the elder Mallory to congratulate him on the splendid son-in-law he was about to acquire—and she couldn't think of any way to avert catastrophe. With Storm wearing a towel and acting the happy fiancé, and she in her gown . . .

Oh, *Lord!* The truth wouldn't be believed—not now, after Storm's announcement. Numbly, she accepted Porter's happy congratulations, aware of Storm's possessive arm and fighting an impulse to elbow him sharply in the ribs. Only dimly hearing Porter's apologies to her "fiancé" for disturbing them so early in the morning, her attention was fully caught when he obligingly suggested that they could talk later—that night, at a party he and his wife were having.

Opening her mouth to refuse the invitation, Casey found herself being subjected to a rib-crushing, one-armed hug, and she promptly forgot what she had been going to say.

"We'd love to, wouldn't we, honey?" Storm said, looking down at her with a glinting smile.

With outward obedience, she parroted faithfully, "We'd love to. Thank you, Dr. Porter."

Five minutes later, Porter was gone, and Casey fiercely shrugged away the possessive arm. "I'm very impressed with your ability to think fast," she told him in a carefully expressionless voice, "but couldn't you come up with a better face-saver? A fake engagement, for God's sake!"

"I thought it was pretty neat myself," Storm remarked calmly, strolling over to sit on the couch, entirely unperturbed by the fact that his towel was coming undone.

Averting her eyes from the positively flaunted masculinity, she began to pace restlessly back and forth. "You don't understand. He will no doubt call my father and tell him."

"So?" Storm was maddeningly unconcerned.

She halted and faced him with a glare. "After the disaster of my first engagement," she told him bitterly, "my father will abandon anything short of a world crisis to come tearing over here and find out what I've gotten myself engaged to *this* time!"

"Thanks a lot."

Ignoring the mildly indignant comment, she began to pace again. "He'll think I've flipped! And so soon after... Dammit, why did you have to get me into this? I'll have to explain another broken engagement, and—"

"You're entirely misreading the situation, honey," Storm interrupted, his smile a strange, casual promise.

Halting, she stared at him. "What are you talking about? My father will—"

"I'm not particularly concerned with what your father will do. If and when he arrives, we probably won't be here anyway, so why worry?"

"Where will we be?" she asked, feeling bizarrely that she had stepped into this movie in the middle of the second reel and that that was why nothing was making sense to her.

"On our honeymoon."

"Are you out of your mind?" Casey remained on her feet by sheer willpower, her knees suddenly turning to liquid.

He laughed softly. "A man in my condition would probably be considered technically insane," he admitted wryly, "but I'm thinking clearly enough."

A man in his condition? What was he talking about? "You—you're not making sense," she said uneasily.

"Sure I am. You see, honey, my announcement to Porter wasn't a lie. Nor was it a face-saver. You and I are going to be married. I told you that I'd stamp Carmichael on you so thoroughly that no other man would come near you. Well, that's what I intend to do. And the best way I can think of is with a wedding ring and a very married look." His eyes glittered with determination and something else, something she couldn't identify. "Give me a few nights, sweetheart, and you'll look so married you'll scare men away from a distance of twenty feet!"

Trying to think clearly and not achieving any very noticeable results, she squeaked, "But I've only known you for two days!"

"Well, I'm not getting any younger, you know, honey."

Casey got a firm grip on herself. He was kidding, of course. He had to be kidding. Or insane. Technically insane? "I don't want to get married, thank you very much. I much prefer single bliss."

"But you haven't sampled wedded bliss yet," Storm pointed out with a gentle smile. "You'll prefer that, honey. In fact, I'll make sure of it."

"You're just trying to punish me, aren't you?" she demanded in a voice of gathering indignation. "You're getting even because I went out with Ham last night!"

He sighed and got to his feet, cinching the towel tighter around his lean waist. "I'm trying to forget about that, honey. But I plan to make damn sure it doesn't happen again."

Casey folded her arms in a defiant and defensive gesture and glared at him. "When are you going to get it through your head that you don't own me? And I'm not going to marry you!"

He sighed again, walking toward her with a curiously cat-footed stride, the light eyes darkening. "There seems to be only one way of reasoning with you, princess."

Too late, Casey guessed his intention, trying to dodge

his seeking hands, her eyes wide. But it was no use. He caught her shoulders firmly, the big hands trapping without hurting. She could feel them burn even through her gown, her own flesh warming instantly in response. Frantically, she pushed against the bare chest, but that was the wrong thing to do.

The crisp hair curling against her palms ignited her senses in a way Casey wouldn't have believed possible, weakness flowing back into her knees and dizziness into her head.

A single breath away from her lips, he murmured huskily, "There comes a time when talking has to stop, my lovely princess. And that's now. Like the man said, actions speak so much louder than words!"

He took her lips then, with a mastery that ignored resistance and demanded response. Neither gentle nor cruel, it was the kiss of a lover, devastating in its intensity. His tongue invaded the sweetness of her mouth in stark possession.

Casey's world reeled in that moment; her arms slipped up around his neck in an attempt to hold on to some small fragment of reality. But reality swiftly became a thing to forget about, because this...whatever it was...was so much sweeter.

His hands moved down her back to her hips, pulling her against him with a crushing desire that would have stolen Casey's breath if she'd had any left. "You're mine," he grated suddenly, tearing his lips from hers, "and soon the whole world will know it! You're going to marry me, Casey."

"No," she protested weakly, her hands denying the protest by locking into his hair to pull him even closer. "No...I can't."

"You can. You will!" he told her fiercely.

Casey stared up at him dazedly, trying to understand his determination, his absolute certainty. She needed time to think, time to find the truth, but he wouldn't allow her that. The hands at her hips pulled her even closer, and, separated only by the towel and the thin silk of her gown, the hardness of his desire brought a rush of fire to her loins.

She gasped when one of his hands slid up over her rib cage to find the heavy firmness of her breast. Sanity went spinning off into nowhere, leaving her with nothing to cling to except this incredible madness. It was Casey who gave in abruptly, her shaking legs carrying her up on tiptoes to fit herself more firmly against his maleness, her hands pulled his head down and her lips seeking his.

She closed her eyes and shut out the world, accepting the invitation of his darting tongue and exploring the warmth of his mouth. She felt his body shudder against hers, and she knew that an answering tremor shook her own slender frame. A small part of her mind was awed by the intensity of her need, shaken by the knowledge that no other man had ever been able to rouse this reponse in her. Not even Roger, with whom she had believed herself to be in love.

His lips trailed fire down her throat, impatiently pushing aside the lacy strap of her gown to explore the delicate bones of her shoulder. "Marry me, Casey," he whispered hoarsely.

She didn't even bother to reply, barely heard him; in fact, her entire concentration focused on this primitive desire to belong to him at all costs. He had the right to make her his, she thought in a sudden rush of understanding. Somehow he had gained that right. She didn't know how, or why, but he had.

But she couldn't marry him. She just couldn't! They had only met two days before, and she didn't even trust him. It could all be just a game to him, a cruel game. But he's not cruel, her mind cried out silently, adding to Casey's confusion.

And her confusion increased tenfold when he suddenly

put her away from him firmly. "You are . . . a stubborn lady, Casey Mallory," he whispered huskily, his lustrous eyes still dark with desire. "I'm going to have my work cut out for me, getting you to the altar."

When he released her, Casey sank bonelessly into the chair behind her, vaguely grateful for the fact of its presence. She stared at him a bit wildly, wanting more than anything else in the world to throw herself into his arms again and plead with him to make love to her. But she knew intuitively that he wouldn't. He made no effort to hide his desire; his ragged breathing and taut muscles were ample evidence of the restraint that had enabled him to pull away.

But he wanted surrender. And Casey knew with a terrible certainty that surrender to this man would have to be unconditional. He would make her his in the most basic way possible . . . and she would never again be free of him.

"What are you going to do?" she whispered, the question making no sense to herself until she heard his answer.

"I'm going to convince you that we belong together," he replied softly, his deep voice gritty with control. "I'm going to make love to you until you're dizzy with desire, until your sleep is filled with dreams of us. I'm going to haunt your days and your nights, until you agree to marry me. I'm going to love you, honey. And I'll teach you to love me. Because I'm a very patient man."

Casey took a deep breath, trying to slow her racing heart. "That—that's absurd. We barely know each other!"

He shrugged. "We have the rest of our lives to get to know each other, sweetheart. Besides, I already know you almost as well as I know myself."

She lifted her chin, an angry sparkle in her green eyes. "I don't believe that!"

Storm folded his arms across his massive chest, one brow lifting with unconscious arrogance. "No? Then I'll prove it to you, Casey. I'll tell you what I know about you. And then maybe you'll realize that I'm not playing games.

"I know that you love your father very much—enough that you've spent your entire life trying to measure up to his standards. I'm willing to bet that he's an autocratic man, probably cold and certainly not demonstrative. You love him, but you've never been able to show that love, and you've never felt that it was returned."

Casey bit her lip to keep from crying out at the truth of his statements, torn between pain and astonishment that he should have been able to guess so much. But he wasn't finished yet.

"I know that you became engaged somewhere around a year ago," he continued evenly. "The man was a fool, a treacherous bastard who used you to gain access to the project you were working on in Virginia. He was probably charming, and you fell in love—or thought you did. All the love bottled up inside you was given to him freely, and he walked all over it. You defended him up until the very end. You believed him and trusted him. Until he left—probably fleeing the country. You knew, then, that he was guilty as sin. And you were left feeling betrayed and ashamed."

Quietly, he added, "You resigned because of that shame—probably helped along by a few blistering words from your father about foolish, weak women in love. And now you're afraid to love . . . and to trust. You don't want to be used again, and you don't want the vulnerability that love brings. And now," he went on without the slightest change in either voice or expression, "if I may borrow your razor, sweetheart, I'd like to shave."

"It's in the top drawer of the vanity," she whispered, then watched silently as he turned and left the room.

Stunned, she couldn't think at all for a long moment. And when her mind did begin working again, her thoughts were disjointed. How did he know? How could he possibly know? Her feelings—right down to the shame and betrayal she had felt when Roger's duplicity had been revealed—Storm had understood.

Desperately, her mind tried and failed to cope with this new understanding. If he knew that much, he'd probably already guessed that she suspected Roger of having something to do with Apollo's problems. And that meant . . . he wasn't trying to trick her. He really wanted to marry her!

But why? Was it only because he wanted her? No, he didn't have to marry her for that. And he knew it as well as she did. Once in his arms, she was powerless to resist him. It couldn't be because he loved her. People just didn't fall in love in the space of two days! But he was so possessive, and so absolutely certain that he wanted marriage . . .

Fiercely, Casey shook the thoughts away. It didn't really matter why he wanted to marry her, because marriage was out of the question. She didn't believe in marrying for any reason other than love, and she had learned her lesson too well to love again.

Frowning slightly, she glanced at the timepiece on the mantel, surprised to realize that barely an hour had passed since she'd shut off her alarm clock. Already, it seemed as if the day had been going on forever.

"And I haven't even had my coffee," she muttered forlornly.

chapter 5

TEN MINUTES LATER, Casey was in the kitchen. Dressed in jeans and a clingy knit sweater, she moved about the room cooking breakfast. Since common sense told her that Storm hadn't gotten so large by eating a slice of toast for his morning meal, she made quite a bit more than her usual breakfast—and she wasn't exactly a toast-and-coffee type herself.

Storm came into the room just as she was spooning generous portions of scrambled eggs onto two plates. "Your cat," he remarked in a mildly complaining tone, "shared my shower. And he sat on the vanity while I shaved."

"You should be flattered," she managed lightly. "You've obviously found a friend."

He sniffed the appetizing aroma in the room and smiled as she placed the plates on the table. "This is nice, honey. But you didn't have to bother; we could have gone out."

Turning away to pour the coffee, she murmured, "Your reward. For cleaning up so nicely last night."

He chuckled softly. "Great. I'll serve you breakfast in bed tomorrow morning."

Choosing to ignore the implications of that, she merely responded, "Oh? Can you cook?"

"I'm pretty good with breakfast," he told her modestly, "and I can broil a steak. Other than that, I'm a little shaky." He waited until she sat down, and then took the chair across from her, saying cheerfully, "It looks terrific, princess."

Casey studied him beneath her lashes as he began to eat, her eyes roving over the stark planes and angles of his face. Again, she admitted to herself that he wasn't handsome—not conventionally so, at any rate. But there was something very attractive, even magnetic, about the harsh features. And those eyes...they were beautiful. If she never saw him again, those compelling eyes would haunt her all the days of her life.

When he looked up suddenly, she dropped her own eyes hastily, fearful that her thoughts could be too easily read.

"You're a good cook," he told her.

"Thanks," she muttered, realizing that she had not tasted her own food.

"You're also very subdued," he added gently. "Was I on target, princess?"

She didn't pretend to misunderstand. Meeting the gleaming eyes openly, knowing that she was vulnerable on this, at least, she said with forced lightness, "Bull's-eye. All the way across the board."

He reached across the table to cover the hand that was toying restlessly with her coffee cup. "And what you suspect about Apollo is that the bastard you were engaged to has something to do with the explosion and the computer's having been tampered with."

Casey half nodded, dropping her eyes again. With a glint of humor, she murmured, "You shouldn't keep calling him that—especially if he shows up around here. Roger's nearly as big as you are, and he knows judo."

"I don't care if he's a giant with an army to back him up," Storm responded calmly. "I'm more motivated than he is. After what he did to you, sweetheart, if I get my hands on the guy, I'll quite probably kill him."

"Don't bother on my account," she said with a faint smile. "A few months ago, I probably would have stood on the sidelines and cheered you on; right now I don't give a particular damn."

His hand tightened on hers. "Then you weren't covering up for him when you refused to tell me what you suspected?"

Honestly startled, she stared at him. "No, of course not! I wouldn't waste a breath to warn him if—if his pants were on fire!"

Storm laughed softly. "Good! But I still want to know why you wouldn't confide in me."

Casey frowned slightly and abruptly pulled her hand from beneath his. "Because it's crazy. That Roger should have anything to do with it, I mean. If he has any sense at all, he's not even in the *country*—let alone up to his old tricks. I'm just being paranoid after the last time, that's all."

He leaned back in his chair and gazed at her, the tiger eyes shrewd. After a long moment, he said a bit grimly, "But you're afraid he'll show up here. You're afraid of *him*. Why, princess?"

Casey didn't really want to answer that, but she had come this far. Far enough to tell him at least part of the truth, anyway. "I wasn't just . . . under suspicion last time, Storm." Her voice was barely audible. "Roger made it look as if I'd taken those documents. He—he planted evidence against me. To give himself time to get out of the country, I suppose. Anyway, I was . . . all but accused of being a traitor. I couldn't go through that again."

"You won't have to, sweetheart; I promise you that." He frowned suddenly. "What about your father? He stood by you, didn't he?"

"Publicly," she murmured.

"But not privately? Hell, he didn't think you'd done it, did he?" Storm sounded disgusted.

She smiled in spite of herself. "He'd be greatly offended if he heard you ask that," she murmured, and then sighed. "In my father's eyes, the only crime I committed was the crime of falling in love. True scientists— particularly women, one can safely assume, since he did love my mother—aren't supposed to do that. And since he hadn't liked Roger in the first place, he was able to add my flaunting of his parental advice to my stupidities."

"No wonder you're afraid to try again," Storm muttered, shaking his head. "Between the two of them, they really messed you up, didn't they, honey?"

"Let's just say that I learned my lesson," she countered lightly, rising and carrying her virtually untouched plate to the sink.

"You learned to be afraid," he responded flatly, and Casey nearly jumped as she realized that he'd followed her across the room. Hands at her small waist, he drew her back against him and then wrapped her in a curiously protective hug. "That means that I have to teach you to trust again . . . to trust me."

Casey allowed herself the luxury of relaxing against him, feeling drained by the confession of details she'd told no one else. She wondered if he knew that she had trusted him that much. She was only just beginning to realize it herself.

"Now tell me the rest, honey," he murmured, bending his head to nuzzle the side of her neck.

"The—the rest?" She heard the betraying huskiness in her voice, and tried to ignore his caressing lips . . . not that she could.

"That bastard hit you," Storm said with gritty certainty. "I want to know about that, Casey."

"There isn't anything to tell," she whispered, wondering if he was that perceptive or if she was just lousy at keeping secrets. "He lost his temper and . . . and he hit me."

Storm's arms tightened around her, and he lifted his head to say tightly, "I hope you're right in your suspicions, honey. Because it would give me the greatest pleasure on earth to wring that bastard's neck!"

Surprised rather than alarmed by the violence in his voice, she turned within the circle of his arms and stared up at him. "He didn't hurt me, Storm—not really. I mean, it didn't make me suspect every other man of wanting to hit me. It just put the crowning touch on my memories, that's all."

He gazed down at her, his golden eyes intense. "You know, don't you, sweetheart, that I would never hit you?"

"I know that." She spoke from an instinct more certain than knowledge could ever be, and she was dimly surprised at her own certainty. "You might very well *punish* me," she added with an ironic smile, "but you wouldn't hit me."

He grinned faintly. "I'm glad to know that you realize the difference!" And then, with a peculiarly savage quietness, he added, "I'd cut my own throat before I'd hurt you, honey."

Casey felt a fluttering sensation somewhere near her heart, and she hastily pulled away from him. "I have to clean up in here. And as good as your clean-up job was last night, the living room carpet still needs to be vacuumed."

Accepting the abrupt change of subject without a blink, he said cheerfully, "I'll do the living room. Where's the vacuum cleaner?"

"Hall closet," she murmured, turning to the sink and

busying herself determinedly. How was she supposed to get this man out of her mind if she couldn't even get him out of her house?

She couldn't.

It was a surprisingly enjoyable day—from Casey's point of view, anyway. She allowed herself to relax totally in his company for the first time, intrigued by the feeling of companionship she had never shared with anyone else. They argued amiably over who would do the crossword puzzle in the morning paper—a habit both shared—and ended up doing it together. They repotted two of the plants uprooted the night before, and then spent an uproarious hour trying to teach Pundit to sit on command—something he adamantly refused to do, even for Storm.

They watched an old British mystery on television, debating over "whodunit" and both ending up wrong. Storm made a trip to the store for steaks at lunchtime, insisting on doing the cooking himself and keeping Casey in stitches with his authoritative lecture on the proper way to toss a salad. Both shared the cleaning chores and then returned to the living room to watch another movie, this time a western. Casey amused Storm by rooting loudly for the Indians and bemoaning the death of a chief she had liked because of his colorful headdress.

A spirited game of Monopoly topped off the afternoon, with blatant cheating going on and a great deal of money and property changing hands. Storm made up the rules—cheerfully ignoring the ones on the inside of the box—displaying the talent of a born usurer and winning the game by an indecent margin.

If it hadn't been for the unsatisfied desire between them and a peculiar little habit of Storm's, Casey could well have forgotten that he had asked her to marry him.

The tension was quite definitely there. In spite of all the laughter and teasing, it took only a lingering glance or touch to call it immediately to mind. It was between them constantly, a feeling of fires smoldering just beneath the surface.

And the habit of Storm's didn't help. He was a *touching* kind of man, she discovered. He literally couldn't pass by her or sit beside her without touching her. Stroking her hair, giving her a hug, taking her hand and rubbing it almost absently against his cheek; he seemed to simply enjoy touching her. The gestures obviously weren't meant to be arousing and yet were just as obviously pleasurable to them both.

For Casey, raised by an undemonstrative father and inherently shy herself, the day was something of a revelation. At first stiffening at his touch, she gradually relaxed, and she even found herself touching him occasionally.

It might have been then that trust began to build, although Casey wasn't consciously aware of it. She only knew that there was something endearing about a man so large and commanding who touched her as though she were a spoiled and petted kitten.

With a reluctance that surprised her, Casey reminded Storm of the party he'd promised they would attend, and pointed out that he had to return to his hotel to change.

"The Porters give formal parties," she told him pointedly. "Mrs. Porter is from Boston, and she has the unshakable conviction that only she can bring civilization to El Dorado."

"You mean I have to rent a tux?" he groaned.

"Rent a tux?" She was startled, thinking of his expensive car. Then a reason occurred to her, and Storm confirmed it with his next words.

With a faint grimace, he muttered, "As you've already noticed, I'm something of a maverick when it comes to clothes. I hate formal-dress occasions. I'm also superstitious. I figure if I don't *have* a dinner jacket, I won't have to wear one very often."

"Oh." Casey stared at him for a moment, her interest

definitely piqued. "Are you really superstitious? You don't look the sort."

"Cross my heart." He did so solemnly. "I'm the seventh son of a seventh son."

"I thought it was the seventh daughter of a seventh daughter."

"In my case, that's physically impossible."

"Cute." She lifted a brow. "Do you really have six brothers?"

"Seven. One came after me. I also have a younger sister."

As an only child, Casey was amazed by the size of his family. *"Nine* kids in your family?"

"Nine," he confirmed, adding with definite relish, "everything's big in Texas."

Casey choked and started to laugh, and his grin didn't help matters. Gaining control of herself, she muttered finally, "Funny. That's funny. Nine kids? Your poor mother."

His grin remained. "You'll like my mother. Every one of her kids is twice her size physically, but she's bigger than all of us. While we were growing up, all she had to do to punish any of us was to frown. We all stayed out of trouble just to see her smile."

Choosing to ignore the implication that she would meet his mother, Casey asked curiously, "And your father?"

"Big, like the rest of us. Cheerful." Casually, Storm added, "He's a doctor."

For some reason, that fact fascinated Casey. "A doctor? Did any of your siblings decide to follow in his footsteps?"

"My sister. She's practicing in Chicago now. The rest of us are scattered all over the country. Various jobs. All married except me."

Deciding to get as far away from *that* subject as possible, Casey hastily steered the conversation back on course. Glancing at her watch, she said brightly, "The party! You'd better head toward your hotel. And whether or not you rent a tux, just remember that if you show up in jeans and a flannel shirt, they won't let you in."

Allowing the change of subject, Storm looked at her speculatively. "What are you going to wear?"

Thinking that she would need all the confidence she could muster if she intended to survive an evening of probable congratulations, Casey answered calmly, "Oh, I have a little something in mind. It's gold, by the way, so don't clash with me."

"I don't trust the look in your eyes," he announced.

Casey guessed that the look gleamed even brighter. "It would serve you right if I dressed up like an Amazon. You know—one of those short little skirts with no top and lots of bangles on my arms."

Storm grinned. "Honey, you can dress up like that for me any time you like. We'll have our own party."

Casey flushed and gave him a shove toward the door, vaguely pleased that she was actually able to budge him an inch or so. "Will you just go, please? I have to get ready."

He caught her hand casually to pull her as far as the door, saying, "We'll have dinner somewhere and then go on to the party, okay, sweetheart? I'll be back to pick you up in a couple of hours." He kissed her lightly on the nose, waved cheerfully, and headed for his car.

Casey watched the car disappear, then went inside, muttering, "Kiss me on the nose, will you? Hah! Just wait 'til tonight!"

It didn't do a bit of good to tell herself that she didn't want to get involved with Storm Carmichael. And she ignored the warning from her saner self about the folly of playing with fire. The only thing that seemed to matter right then was her sudden, intense desire to rock Storm off his balance for once.

* * *

Nearly two hours later, Casey stood before the full-length mirror in her bedroom, fraught with a sudden feeling of uncertainty. The "little something" was indeed gold; it was made of a silky material that glittered like the real thing. All similarity to the metal ended right there. The dress was vaguely Grecian in design, leaving one shoulder and most of her back bare, and it clung like a living thing to her curvacious body. It was calf-length and slit up one side nearly to the hip.

Casey had bought the dress on a brief trip to New York more than a year before, but she'd never found the occasion or the nerve to wear it. She wasn't certain that she could carry it off tonight. Having experienced one of Mrs. Porter's parties, she wasn't afraid of being overdressed, but she was nervous about Storm's reaction.

The woman in her, stubbornly refusing to think of the possible consequences, wanted to provoke a reaction from him. Was that so unreasonable? She simply wanted to see him—for once—lose that incredible mastery over himself. It was not only playing with fire, she knew; it was, in fact, playing with fire in a room full of dynamite. But there was a certain exhilaration in living dangerously. Especially after a life with rigid rules and logical decisions.

But she still wasn't sure about that dress. Her hair looked good, piled loosely on top of her head with a few simple strands providing a softening frame for her face. And the delicate Italian sandals on her feet added just the right touch. Careful makeup had given her eyes an exotic, mysterious quality, and her skin was still smooth and golden from its summer tan. But that dress...

Giving in suddenly to a cowardly impulse, Casey turned to the closet and removed a black satin blazer. To her surprise, the blazer turned her outfit from eye-catchingly sexy to coolly sophisticated. There! Now, if she could only gather up the nerve to remove the blazer at some point during the evening...

The doorbell rang as she was picking up her gold evening purse, and she made her way down the hall, disturbed by the prickle of excitement she felt.

"I've reserved a table for seven o'clock, honey, and it's nearly that now, so we'd better—" he began as soon as she opened the door. He halted abruptly, his shining eyes roving over her.

Casey was more than a little surprised herself. He had apparently rented a dinner jacket after all. It was off-white, which went very well with his deep tan and copper hair, and it fit his broad shoulders perfectly.

He reached up suddenly, one hand warmly cupping the side of her neck, breathing almost soundlessly. "God, but you're beautiful!" And then his lips were moving over hers with shattering gentleness.

Not even bothering with a token resistance, Casey stood perfectly still, her free hand lifting to touch his cheek lightly. She was almost afraid to touch him, afraid that any movement might disturb the magic of this moment. But her hand moved of its own volition, needing the fleeting contact.

Her instant response wrenched a deep groan from Storm, and he lifted his head to mutter hoarsely, "Let's skip the party."

Bemused, Casey gazed up at him with an uncertain little smile. "You were the one who promised we'd come," she reminded him.

The golden eyes went very bright suddenly, and he raised his free hand to cover the one still touching his cheek. "Is that regret I hear, sweetheart? Have you stopped running from me?"

Her eyes shifted away from his in confusion, and she hastily pulled her hand away. "We'd better go," she murmured.

He laughed softly, ruefully. "Well, a man can always hope." He stepped back to allow her to come out and close the door, then he drew her hand through the crook of his arm and led her to his car.

Storm easily recaptured the companionship of the day during the ride to the restaurant and their meal by going into great detail about the trials and tribulations of renting a tux on extremely short notice. He also had a few unkind things to say about shops that didn't cater to large men.

Wine was served liberally with their meal, and by the time they were back in the Ferrari and heading for the party, Casey was feeling more than a little reckless. Wine generally had that effect on her, and she knew that the coming party would only increase her daring. Not that she minded. It was nice to let her hair down for once and tempt the fates... and maybe a tiger-eyed Viking as well.

"What are you going to tell Dr. Porter about the break-in?" she asked, only mildly interested.

He reached over to pat her silk-covered knee comfortingly. "I won't mention the possibility of Collins's having anything to do with it, if that's what worrying you, sweetheart. I'll tell him just what we told the police: that whoever broke into your house was obviously looking for something, probably the timer. He can do his own explaining about why Apollo didn't report to the police that that explosion was no accident."

Vaguely aware that something was wrong with his comments, she mulled them over silently for a moment. Then she had it. "Collins. How do you know Roger's last name? I didn't tell you."

"Porter told me." Storm's voice was casual. "Your father must have mentioned it."

"Oh." Casey said no more as the car drew up in the Porters' drive. But the mention of her father made her, if anything, even more reckless. She was going to enjoy tonight. Not even the thought of her so-called engagement to Storm had the power to daunt her. She would worry about that later.

The house was ablaze with lights as they walked up the sidewalk, and Casey wondered for the first time just who would be at this party. She had done very little socializing since moving to El Dorado four months before, and, other than the Apollo employees, she knew very few people. Judging by Mrs. Porter's last party, it would be a glittering event.

Casey knew that her thoughts had been on target when the front door was opened by the butler, revealing a colorful crowd that seemed to fill the entire lower floor of the large three-story home. The guests were obviously not the staid, middle-aged crowd one might have expected Mrs. Porter to cultivate, but were instead a mixed bag of ages and professions. And all were dressed to the teeth.

"You weren't kidding about formal," Storm muttered into her ear.

"You can't say you weren't warned," she muttered in reply, smiling at the butler as he let them in.

"Your jacket, Miss?"

Obligingly, Casey allowed Storm to slip her jacket off and hand it to the butler. She accepted a drink from a passing maid and then turned back to Storm, having honestly forgotten the brevity of her dress. Biting back a giggle at his expression she observed sweetly, "Your mouth is open."

The mouth snapped shut. "Tell me something," he requested a bit tightly. "Are you wearing anything under that—that handkerchief?"

The bluntness of his question was characteristic and didn't surprise Casey. She was just glad he kept his voice low—although she had a feeling it was due to temper rather than circumspection. The golden eyes were flashing like railway semaphores.

Innocently, she asked, "Don't you like my dress?"

"Casey—" he began warningly, then broke off abruptly as Porter hailed them across the room. "I'll deal with you later," he added in a low voice.

"Promises, promises," she murmured.

"Dammit, Casey, don't say things like that when—"

"Casey! Carmichael, glad you could come!" Porter was effusive in his welcome. "Make yourselves at home." In a harassed voice, he went on, "Carmichael, I've gotten three calls today from the Chairman of the Board; he wants to know what the hell's going on. I'm sure Casey will excuse us while we go into my den and talk about this."

"Of course," Casey assured them with a serene smile. "You two go on; I'll just mingle."

Obviously mistrusting her smile, Storm nonetheless had no option but to follow his host from the room. Putting his last warning look from her mind, Casey drifted into the hub of the party.

The dress, she discovered almost at once, was a great conversation starter. Not that it was mentioned by any of the three men who converged on her the moment Storm disappeared from sight. But since each of them had trouble keeping their eyes on her face, Casey assumed it was the dress.

She didn't feel the least bit uncomfortable in flirting with the three men who nearly fell all over each other introducing themselves. As a matter of fact, she enjoyed the situation immensely.

It might have been the wine. Or the first drink—which was rapidly exchanged for a second one. It might have been the ghost of her father, frowning disapprovingly over her shoulder. It might have been any one or all of those things that made her so audacious...except that it wasn't.

She was talking lightly to her new friends when a heavy arm fell across her shoulders and a cool voice said, "I'm sorry I was so long, darling. Miss me?"

"Extremely," Casey replied lightly, with a sarcasm meant only for Storm's ears. Sipping her drink, she nearly hooted as her "friends" rapidly made themselves scarce—

encouraged, no doubt, by Storm's somewhat forbidding expression. "And I didn't even get a chance to introduce you," she murmured.

"Did you know them?" he asked dryly, turning her to face him.

"Well, I do now."

He sighed, taking the half-finished drink from her hand and setting it on the tray of a passing maid. "I think you're a bit tipsy, princess," he informed her.

"I am no such thing," she responded with great dignity. "I'm simply having a good time. That's what parties are for, right? To have a good time."

"You need a watchdog," he said, ignoring her defense.

"Nonsense!" Casey shrugged off his hand and straightened to her full height, unconsciously causing a nearby man to choke on his drink as he observed the spectacle of Casey apparently in imminent danger of parting company with her dress.

Storm actually paled. "Casey, for God's sake—" he began, and was interrupted yet again by Dr. Porter.

"Carmichael, I want you to meet my wife. And, Amy, you've already met Casey, of course."

"Of course!" Mrs. Porter answered brightly, her rather girlish voice perfectly matched to her tiny, fragile appearance. She beamed at the tall couple before her, her hand lost in the clasp Storm offered. "Why, you're perfectly matched! James has been telling me about your whirlwind romance."

"More like a hurricane," Casey murmured.

"What was that, dear?" Mrs. Porter asked.

Relenting when she noticed the warning glitter in Storm's eyes, Casey said sweetly, "Oh, I was just agreeing with you—about the whirlwind romance, I mean. He swept me right off my feet!"

"Have you set a date yet?"

Casey opened her mouth to reply, but Storm cut in

neatly. "Not yet, but I'm sure it'll be soon." He slipped an arm around Casey's waist, drawing her near. "Right, darling?"

Casey's smile probably looked loving, but she meant Storm to know that it promised great things along the lines of revenge. And she didn't say a word. She didn't trust herself to.

The Porters drifted away a few minutes later, but before Casey could utter a syllable about their bogus engagement, Storm was pulling her toward the entrance hall. Loath to cause a scene, she smilingly hissed, "Where are we going?"

"That's up to you." He stopped in the hall, facing her. "Either you put your jacket on—now, or we leave—now."

Flushing, she said mutinously, "That's ridiculous! There's absolutely nothing wrong with my dress!"

"Nothing except the fact that every man here has been ogling you since you removed that jacket. It's beautiful, princess, and you wear it like a queen—but I've discovered, somewhat to my surprise, that I'm a jealous man. And watching men watching you is sending my blood pressure through the roof. Now, are you going to get the jacket, or shall I?"

Surprised, Casey realized that he really was angry, although he was controlling it very well. His temper sparked her own. Lifting her chin, she told him fiercely, "I won't be dictated to! If I want to wear a—a sheet, then I will!"

"The jacket, Casey."

Glaring at him, she snapped, "You have no right—"

"But I do," he interrupted, lowering his voice abruptly as a couple passed him. Continuing softly, he said, "I have a right. It isn't a right you gave me; it's a right I took. You belong to me, Casey, and I'll make you admit it. I'll make love to you until you can't think straight, until you're in exactly the same condition I'm in now!

But I'll make you admit the right I have, honey. And your little games tonight have made me all the more impatient to do just that."

Something in his eyes shook Casey to the core, both her temper and her recklessness fading fast. "Games? What are you talking about?"

"You know what I'm talking about." His voice was suddenly husky, the golden eyes darkening. "I told you that I wanted you to be sure of me before I made you mine in every sense of the word, and you've been pushing me, Casey. All evening, you've made promises with your eyes, promises you have no intention of delivering. I think I warned you before: my patience has its limits. I may decide to take what I can get."

The middle of a party was not exactly the best place to conduct such a discussion, and the next moment proved it. A tiny brunette approached them, placing her hand with possessive familiarity on Storm's arm and saying sweetly, "Storm, whatever are you doing in El Dorado?"

"Hello, Darleen." Storm almost automatically released Casey, turning his attention to the brunette.

"The last time I saw you, it was in Texas," she said with a breathless little laugh, the brown eyes gazing meltingly into his.

Casey hated her. She stood silently, staring at someone who was obviously an old friend of Storm's . . . and she hated her. The intensity of her own emotions surprised her, not least because never in her life had she been either jealous or possessive. Almost hypnotized, she watched the long, red-polished nails moving on Storm's arm, and inside her head someone was screaming silently, *Leave him alone, damn you—he's mine!*

Gasping soundlessly, she stepped back away from the two, who were still talking, and found a maid to direct her to the powder room. She made her way to the room, grateful to find it empty, and sank down on a satin boudoir chair.

She didn't look into the mirror; she didn't need the reflection to tell her what she already knew. She'd known it all along, really. Since the very first. But that didn't make it any easier to accept.

But perhaps she was wrong. Dr. Mallory had, after all, raised a logical daughter. He had taught her to use her *mind,* and to mistrust the wishes of her heart. And wasn't that the wisest course? She had ignored his teachings once, impulsively giving her heart. And that mistake had nearly cost a career...not to mention what it had done to her ability to trust and to love.

She couldn't make another mistake like that. Not again. She had learned from the last one. Of course she had learned!

Squaring her shoulders, Casey rose from her chair and went to find her blazer. Her mind jeered at her for obeying Storm's command, but she ignored the mental voice. Irritably, she blamed her dress for starting the whole thing. If only she had worn something different. If she had worked and lived somewhere besides Arkansas. If only she had...

Halfway down the stairs, wearing her blazer, she paused as Storm, standing alone at the bottom of the stairs, looked up and saw her. And...dear God...she had done it again.

She had fallen in love.

chapter 6

IT HADN'T BEEN very much of a fight, and already she had surrendered. But it was a surrender she would hide at all costs. Never again would she make herself vulnerable to a man that way. After all, it wasn't as if she needed a man. She could make it alone. She had her career, the respect of her coworkers, plenty of opportunities to accept a date for dinner or whatever. She didn't need a man permanently in her life. Making decisions for her. Telling her what she could or couldn't wear. Calling her princess...

Wiping the disjointed thoughts from her mind, Casey continued steadily down the stairs. She kept her face expressionless with an effort, knowing there was a stiffness in her manner but hoping that Storm would attribute it to sheer anger.

The golden eyes took in the jacket with a satisfied gleam. "Hi, princess. I wondered where you'd gotten to."

"Now you know." Casey halted on the bottom step, the added height putting her on eye level with him. "I was obeying orders, master," she went on in a coolly flippant voice.

His smile faded, and he reached to cover her hand on the banister. "Casey, I wasn't trying to dominate you."

She knew that. She knew very well why he had ordered her to put the jacket on, and, in other circumstances, she would have been flattered. But she needed a wedge to drive between them, and this was the best one she could come up with on the spur of the moment. He was a possessive man; she refused to become a possession.

"I believe you told me that once before," she said calmly. "I didn't believe it then, and I don't now."

He swore softly, staring at her. "How can I make you understand? I respect your independence, honey, I really do. And I know damn well that you're not going to be a meekly obedient wife. I wouldn't want you to be! But I will not have other men stripping you with their eyes— and heaven knows that's likely to happen even when you're decently dressed!"

"Then what are you going to do?" She pulled her hand from beneath his, angry now and not entirely pretending. "Hypothetically speaking, of course. Suppose we *did* get married, Storm—what then? Would you expect me to give up my career? I'm surrounded by men most of the time, you know. Would you tag along every day to make sure no one got out of line, or would you trust me to handle it? Or would I sit at home and file my nails, letting a damned expensive education go to waste? Which would it be?"

The formidable jaw tightened. "You'll work if you want to work, Casey. And I have complete confidence in your ability to handle the men you work with. But at a party like this, every single man and half the married ones are on the make, and you know that as well as I do."

Casey ignored the logic, which she understood, and

fastened instead on the troubling question in her mind. "You're a hypocrite," she told him quietly. "You expect me to trust you completely, and yet you refuse to give me the same trust."

"I'll trust you when you commit yourself, Casey," he said levelly. "Right now you're fighting me, and you're ruthless enough to use another man in that fight. I won't allow that."

Casey shoved her hands into the pockets of the blazer, feeling suddenly off balance and uncertain. "I'm not ruthless."

"Yes, you are, honey." His voice gentled, the tawny eyes holding that peculiar glimmer that made her at once uneasy and excited. "You're beautiful, intelligent, temperamental, passionate. Utterly feminine, although you try to hide it. And ruthless as hell. You're strong enough to take what you want, brave enough to fight for it. The only reason you're confused now about what you want is that Collins's betrayal short-circuited all your instincts."

Was that the problem? she wondered, disturbed. Had Roger's deception scrambled up her instincts until she no longer trusted herself? Trying to fight her own uncertainty, she pushed the troubling questions aside and stepped around him to head back toward the den. "There's a party going on, if you remember," she pointed out politely. "And we're being very rude."

He put a casually possessive arm around her shoulders and fell into step beside her. "One of these days," he said whimsically, "I'm going to cure you of this habit of running away from our little confrontations."

Little? Casey's hurricane analogy came back to her with a vengeance. This peculiar, unsettled feeling: just so would she feel if she were trapped in the eye of a hurricane. The odd thing was that she didn't know if Storm was the hurricane itself or simply the catalyst. But if he was the catalyst, then he stood in no danger of being consumed by the reaction he sparked. She did, though. She could very easily be destroyed.

As they rejoined the party, it immediately became apparent that the Porters had been spreading the news of their engagement. People Casey didn't even know came up to congratulate them, and she was more than a little annoyed by Storm's response. He was the epitome of a man in love. Possessive, attentive, showering her with endearments and loving touches; he played the role as though he were born to it.

Although she didn't touch another drink, Casey's recklessness returned full force. Determined to shake him off his balance, she turned the tables on him. With sweet endearments and loving touches of her own, she rapidly convinced everyone in the room that, in her eyes, Storm was the only man alive.

It didn't shake him at all. The evening became, instead, a curious, subtle game of one-upmanship, a silent battle of wills and talents. No matter how outrageously loving Casey became, Storm topped her easily, his own comments becoming so intimate that she saw more than one listener go wide-eyed with shock.

Casey found herself torn between frustration and amusement, casting about in her keen mind for something to silence, once and for all, this maddening man. The idea that ultimately occurred to her gave her pause for a moment, but she threw discretion to the winds, her entire will set on discomfiting Storm.

"Darling," she implored sweetly, making certain that her voice carried at least to those nearby, "do you think we could leave now? We don't want to be too tired when we get home..." She didn't even have to let her voice trail off suggestively; everyone got the message. She saw startled blinks and hastily hidden grins, and thought, *There! That should get him!*

She should have known better. She really should have.

"Anything you say, sweetheart!" Storm responded

cheerfully, his amber eyes holding a gleam that anyone could have read. And then he showed her just how thoroughly the best-laid plans could go awry.

Before Casey could do more than gasp in shock, she found herself flung over Storm's shoulder as though she weighed nothing. And it wasn't only her upside-down position that caused the blood to rush suddenly to her face. Staring at the back of Storm's coat, feeling his forearm clamped firmly just below the swell of her hips, she only vaguely heard him call for someone to find her purse. Nor did she really hear him telling an obviously shocked host and hostess good night. But she did hear one of the guests exclaim, in a laughing voice, "Good heavens! What an exit!"

She had to agree; it was a spectacular exit. And Storm had quite effectively proven his ability to win any war she cared to declare. To the victor go the spoils—and he was carrying his home over his shoulder.

His victim remained uncharacteristically silent until they were in the car, and then spent a few moments waiting for the dizziness of being suddenly upright again to fade. Sitting on her own side of the car where Storm had gently set her, Casey silently counted until she could trust herself to speak calmly.

"That," she managed at last, "was a sneaky, low-down, underhanded trick!"

"You asked for it, honey." He was obviously unrepentant.

Her sense of fair play reluctantly agreed with him. And, to her astonishment, she found that she was choking back laughter. "Oh, Storm," she moaned, "how could you *do* that?"

"It wasn't very hard," he explained gravely.

"Dammit, you know what I mean! How am I supposed to look Dr. Porter in the eye after tonight? I've spent four months showing him that my mind is securely wrapped in gray flannel, and you—"

"You started it, sweetheart."

"I did not!" she objected immediately. *"You* were the one carrying on like the sultan with his favorite harem girl!"

He laughed softly. "Well, you weren't exactly acting prim and proper, honey. As a matter of fact, I was quite shocked at some of your more suggestive remarks."

"You were not," she retorted irritably. "You enjoyed the whole thing. And don't try to deny it! I don't know how in the world I'm going to explain that exit to Porter."

"You won't have to," Storm told her carelessly. "Mrs. Porter might have been mildly shocked, but old James himself gave me a wink as I was carrying you out. We men understand these things."

Casey thought about lecturing him on the male chauvinistic aspects of that remark, but she was too fascinated with the mental picture of Dr. Porter winking. Solemn Dr. Porter!

She said nothing more until they were walking up toward her house, and then asked in an aggrieved tone, "I suppose you're coming in?"

The injured dignity was wasted on him. "Of course I'm coming in, princess. You and I have something to settle."

"Settle?" She looked at him warily as he unlocked the door, then moved ahead of him into the living room and turned on a lamp. "What are you talking about?"

"You know what I'm talking about." He dropped her keys onto the little Oriental table. "You've been pushing me, honey. And after I warned you, too."

Before Casey's startled eyes, he casually removed his jacket and flung it carelessly over a chair, then began on his tie. The warning! She had forgotten all about it. Or had she? Nervously, Casey took a step backward. "Storm . . . ? You're not—you're not—"

"Yes, I am," he told her pleasantly, the golden eyes

glittering. His tie joined the discarded jacket, and the deft brown fingers began on the buttons of his white shirt. "I think that once I'm in your bed, princess, you won't be quite so confused—about anything."

Casey felt her body betraying her, reacting to the promise in his eyes, but she tried to fight it. "You said you'd give me time! That you wanted me to be sure of you!"

"I changed my mind," he responded simply. "All evening, I've watched you act like a woman in love. Little caresses, teasing words, provocative smiles. You play the role beautifully, honey. Now let's see you follow through."

Was he going to strip right there in front of her? Her mind answered the silent question immediately: of course he would! Green eyes searched frantically for an escape route but discovered that he was between her and the hall. And since the back door led to a fenced yard, there was no escape there. She backed away tensely as he came toward her, leaving his shirt unbuttoned. He was stalking her, dammit!

"Storm, wait! We've only known each other three days!"

"Four," he said calmly, still stalking. "It's after midnight. I should have ignored my gentlemanly impulses and taken you to bed that first day. We'd be married by now."

"No, we wouldn't!" she yelped, trying a feint and then a dash around the couch. Storm read her mind with his uncanny accuracy, ignoring the feint and catching her before she could put the couch between them.

He easily removed the blazer from her struggling body, bending his head to press warm lips to the exposed flesh of her shoulder, and Casey felt her will to resist him dying. Oh, God, it was always this way when he touched her! She was weak, weak!

"Let me love you, Casey," he murmured huskily, his fingers releasing her hair from its confining pins. "I need you so badly. I ache for you."

His words were a potent stimulant to her senses, and Casey closed her eyes as the room seem to reel about her. She felt his hands cupping her face gently, his mouth brushing her eyelids, her nose, the curve of her cheek. He ignored the unconscious invitation of her parted lips, teasing and tormenting until she finally moaned softly and slid her arms up around his neck, her lips searching blindly for his.

With a laugh deep in his throat, Storm gave in to her silent plea, kissing her with a demand that stopped just short of ruthlessness. His mouth moved on hers hungrily, the big hands moving down her back to pull her firmly against him.

Casey had long since stopped protesting. The only sound she made was a murmur of satisfaction when he swept her up into his arms and started down the hallway. She absently nudged off her sandals as they entered the bedroom, letting them fall where they would.

Storm set her on her feet by the bed, reaching to turn on the lamp on the nightstand, then flinging back the covers with an impatient hand. Her dress was dealt with swiftly, and he groaned softly when he saw that she wore absolutely nothing beneath it.

Casey felt herself being lifted and placed gently on the bed, and then she clung fiercely to his neck when he would have drawn away. Vividly in her mind was the memory of the last time he had begun to make love to her. "No!" she gasped huskily. "Dammit, you're not leaving me this time!"

The tawny eyes glimmered with a male satisfaction that Storm made no effort to hide. "I'm not leaving you, sweetheart." He dropped a hard, possessive kiss on her quivering lips and then straightened up by the bed, beginning to rapidly strip off his remaining garments.

Casey watched, intrigued by the way the lamplight played over the rippling muscles of his body. She felt drugged, weak, bemused by the realization that he was beautiful in a way she had never known before. Primitive, compelling, fiercely male.

With his eyes fixed on her, Storm could hardly help noticing her absorbed interest. "Enjoying yourself, honey?" he teased gently.

She found a small laugh from somewhere as he came down on the bed beside her. "You're too self-assured as it is," she complained, amused. "I'm not about to bolster your ego."

His chuckle died abruptly in his throat as he raised himself on one elbow to stare down at her. "You're so marvelously beautiful," he whispered. "I'll never get enough of you, Casey—never!" As if eager for the taste of her, he bent his head suddenly, his mouth trailing fire down her throat. His fingers coaxed first one nipple and then the other out of hiding, and then his mouth took over. Sucking gently, his tongue flicking back and forth erotically, he seemed ravenously hungry for her.

Casey bit her lip with a ragged moan, her fingers tangling in his copper hair. She was both excited and frightened by the sensations rushing through her body, dimly surprised at the strength of her own need. Hesitantly, she explored the corded strength of his neck, the muscle-padded shoulders, loving the feel of firm, smooth flesh beneath her fingers.

And then, suddenly, a face swam before her inner eye, a face stiff with an emotion she only now recognized as distaste—distaste for the passion she had tried to show her fiancé. That reaction had taught her to hide what she felt, to mistrust the strong emotions within herself. It was wrong—wrong for her to feel this way! Tension stole into her body; her hands fell away from Storm.

Reading her mind again, he lifted his head to order fiercely, "Don't think about him, dammit! Think about me—about us! Let yourself feel, darling. Don't be ashamed of the passion inside of you!" He took her hand, placing it on his body. "Touch me, Casey—feel the need I have for you."

Casey could feel him tremble at her touch, could see the naked longing he made no effort to hide. That vulnerability, his willingness to open up to her that way, made her forget everything except their mutual need. She wanted to belong to him, and she no longer fought that knowledge . . . or that need.

Banked-up passion burst suddenly into flame as she lifted her hands to his neck, pulling his head down and arching her body against his in an instinctive movement. He was lying half on top of her now, and Casey happily absorbed the heavy, wonderful weight of him, feeling an intense desire to become a part of him, to lose her separate identity and merge with his.

"I knew it!" There was a soft, savage elation in his deep voice as he felt her uninhibited response. "I knew there was a passion in you to match my own!" His lips feathered lightly along her jaw. "Give yourself to it, Casey. Give yourself to *me!*"

She felt one of his hands beneath her neck, lifting her face for his kiss, the other hand tracing a disturbing pattern on the sensitive skin beneath her breasts. Obeying the command in his voice as well as the desire she had already admitted to, Casey let herself go completely. Her shaking hands moved instinctively over his taut body, exploring the hard planes and angles even as her tongue explored the hungry warmth of his mouth.

He used one foot to draw her legs slowly apart, opening her trembling warmth to the probing, caressing touch of his hand. She gasped when his mouth left hers to slide hotly down to capture a tingling nipple, her fingers digging unconsciously into the muscles of his shoulders.

He was so close, so close to . . . She didn't know. She was only aware of a strange, mysterious feeling building inside of her, a peculiar, shimmering tension. It was like nothing she had ever felt before, and she was suddenly desperately afraid of losing this indescribable sensation. "Oh! Please, Storm . . ." She didn't recognize the husky, tremulous sound of her voice, or even know what she was pleading for.

He lifted his head to stare down at her wide-eyed expression, his own tiger eyes slitted, a curious half-smile on his face. "Tell me what you want, sweetheart," he commanded softly, his fingers teasing, tormenting. "Tell me!"

"You!" She moaned raggedly, pulling at his shoulders, needing to feel the weight of him bearing her down into the bed. "Take me, Storm, please!"

"No, sweetheart," he murmured hoarsely, his hand leaving her thighs and his heavy body replacing it. *"You take me!"*

It seemed a peculiar thing to say, but Casey wasn't really listening to the words. She was listening to the blood rushing through her veins, listening to the pounding of her heart and his. But most of all, she was listening to the clamoring of her senses.

He moved suddenly, strongly, and she cried out softly without meaning to, overwhelmed by a primordial feeling of being possessed, of being *known*.

There was nothing in her experience to relate this to, nothing to prepare her for the incredible feeling of one-ness. She was no longer a separate being, but a part of one. It hadn't been this way with Roger, she thought dimly, and then dismissed that from her mind. Roger wasn't important now.

She clung to Storm fiercely, arching her body against his in a movement that made him shudder and groan, using the strength of her body to possess him as completely as he had possessed her.

After that, there was no rational thought. Guided by his hands, and her own instincts, Casey discovered an enchantment she wouldn't have believed possible. Like an ocean's tide, wave after wave of feeling swept her, each sensation more cataclysmic than the last. She cried out his name at the height of her excitement, only dimly aware of his groaning out her own name.

In a damp tangle of arms and legs, they recovered their breath, hearts gradually returning to normal. Casey was oddly moved by the fact that he didn't release her, even now, but held her in his arms as if he would never let her go.

She summoned the breath for speech. "I have been ravished," she announced, her voice heavy with an exhaustion that was as sweet as it was devastating. "Completely against my will."

He gently pinched one rounded hip. "What was that, princess?" he teased.

"Partially against my will, then," she amended solemnly.

This time, the pinch was a bit sharper. "Try again," he suggested with a smothered laugh.

Casey giggled in spite of herself. "All right then, beast," she murmured, experimentally tasting the warm flesh of his throat. "I was willing. But I was definitely ravished. I may never move again." He tasted wonderful, she thought vaguely. Salty and tangy.

He was chuckling softly. "Never move again, huh? Shall I show you how wrong you are, princess?"

She trailed one hand languidly over his hard-muscled chest, fascinated by the springy red-gold hair and beginning to feel quite energetic. It might have had something to do with the strong hands moving over her back and hips. Her fingers found a flat male nipple, taking care with her long nails and tugging gently.

Storm rolled over suddenly, pulling her on top of him. "I think," he murmured roughly, "that I'm going to be losing sleep for a very long time, princess. I can't seem to keep my hands off you."

Lifting her face from his neck, Casey smiled down at him, her fingers still tugging, teasing. "That's because you have a basic personality flaw," she told him gravely.

His lips quirked in amusement. "And what's that?"

"Greed."

He swatted her lightly on the bottom. "Witch! I'll punish you for that. Just as soon as my strength comes back."

"First I was a princess, now I'm a witch." She traced the outline of his lips slowly, shivering when he drew her finger into his mouth. "Make up your mind."

"You're both," he told her huskily, pressing a kiss into the palm of her hand. "An Amazon princess, tall and strong and beautiful, moving with a grace and dignity that could easily turn a king's head. And a witch...weaving spells with green eyes and a voice that sounds like nothing else on this earth, a voice filled with all sorts of subtle shades and meanings that turn ordinary words into something magical. A man could easily lose his will listening to that voice...and lose his soul in those eyes."

Casey swallowed hard, staring at him. He was doing it again, she realized vaguely. Saying astonishingly sweet things that sounded impossibly sincere. "You know," she murmured at last, "I have never heard a man talk the way you do."

Holding her hand against his cheek, he murmured teasingly, "Have you ever met a man like me before?"

"You have a point." She felt a smile tugging at her lips. "Your mother named you well: you're every bit as unpredictable as a storm."

He smiled oddly. "Storms can be predicted up to a point—if you understand them, that is."

"But that's just it," she murmured, more than half seriously. "I don't understand you."

"There's nothing complex or subtle about me, honey." He released her hand, his fingers gently smoothing the frown between her brows. "What you see is exactly what I am."

Casey didn't believe that. There was always more to a man than the surface revealed. But she didn't want to think about that now. She didn't want to start doubting her own instincts again.

Aware of the stirring of his body and the renewed desire in her own, she lowered her head, her lips finding the masculine nipple that her fingers had been toying with all this time. She nibbled gently, using her teeth and her tongue, hoping to arouse him as he had aroused her earlier. And succeeding.

He groaned softly, his fingers tangling in her honey-colored hair as he stared into the depths of her eyes. "I believe," he muttered hoarsely, "that my energy level is increasing dramatically."

"Really?" Unconsciously provocative, Casey licked her lips. "Maybe we should find some other way of...um...using all that excess energy...?"

"Excess, hell," he growled, pulling her head forward. "I'm damn sure going to have to eat my Wheaties in the morning!"

Casey found herself giggling, her breath mingling with his, delighting in the humor he never seemed to lose. And then he was kissing her deeply, and humor fled. There was only the desire, which never seemed to build slowly, but rather to explode inside her like a wild and uncontrollable nova.

The tawny eyes gleamed between slitted lids when he at last allowed her to raise her head. "Your turn," he murmured, his hands falling away from her.

Willing but uncertain, she looked at him doubtfully. "I—I don't know..." she began hesitantly.

"You know." He smiled slowly. "You've always known. Let yourself go, sweetheart. Let yourself go."

To her surprise, Casey found that she did know how

to please him. Following her instincts, guided by his hoarse groans of pleasure, his muttered encouragement, she explored his body slowly.

Knowing that she would dominate only because he allowed her to, she took full advantage of the opportunity. There was a peculiar pleasure in having him at her mercy, even temporarily. And there was an even greater pleasure in knowing that she could arouse him, feel his body tremble, hear his breath grow ragged. With a giddy sense of power, she went a little crazy, desperate to learn every inch of him. She teased with her hands, raking her nails gently over clenching muscles. Her mouth searched, tasting and exploring. Her body moved with a sensuousness she had not known she possessed.

And then, suddenly, the room swung crazily, and her murmur of protest died in her throat as he rose above her. "Tell me what you feel," he ordered tautly, his hands and lips taking over to caress her restless body. "Tell me, Casey!"

"I feel . . . I'm burning," she whispered huskily, arching her body with a moan when his mouth found the hardened tip of one breast. "I'm on fire!" A part of her wanted to scream at him to stop this exquisite torture; another part wanted to plead with him never to stop.

"God, you're wonderful," he muttered thickly. "So warm and passionate." He settled himself between her thighs once more, claiming her with a curious mixture of passion and tenderness.

Casey gasped as he began to move, holding him, moving with him. That astounding tension was building within her again, transporting her to a wonderous, enchanted place. She climbed higher and higher, the splintering tension becoming a pleasure so intense it was almost painful, a spellbinding agony shooting through every nerve of her body.

And then she was floating, suspended somewhere between heaven and earth, sobbing out his name. She felt the shuddering of his body only dimly as she clung to him, refusing to let him leave her.

It was a long time before either of them could move, and then it was Storm who rolled slowly over, still with her, still holding her. He reached down to pull the covers up over their cooling bodies, and Casey murmured almost inaudibly, "Stay with me," not wanting to lose this special closeness.

"I will, honey." He turned off the lamp on the nightstand, then drew her even closer, kissing her forehead gently. "You'll never get rid of me now."

Casey had never felt so weary . . . or so utterly content. Fleetingly, she remembered that first day, and something he had told her. He'd been right, after all, she thought drowsily. He had taken her . . . and there wasn't a doubt in her mind about it.

It was the sun that woke her, and Casey turned her head fretfully to avoid that irritating glare, reluctant as always to open her eyes and face the day. But there was a niggling sense of unease in her mind, something she felt she ought to remember. And there was a curious ache in her body. Not painful, exactly—just different. Unusual.

Her outflung arm explored the bed beside her, finding it empty and not sure why that didn't feel right. Then her eyes snapped open, staring at the dented pillow beside her own. And she remembered.

She sat bolt upright, clutching the sheet to her breasts and staring around her bedroom. Empty, except for her. A glance at the clock on the nightstand told her only that she'd forgotten to wind the damn thing the night before. Not surprising, really. But the sun was high in the sky, so it was probably around noon.

Casey tilted her head, listening. Nothing. The house was as quiet as a tomb. Probably as empty as her bedroom . . . and her bed. "Well, dammit," she muttered miserably, leaning back against her pillow, "he could have said goodbye."

A sneering little voice in her head reminded her that Storm had gotten what he'd wanted; why should he stick around? She ignored the voice. He wasn't like that. So where was he?

"Good morning, princess!"

The cheerful voice caused her to jump and then relax as tension flowed from her body. He was standing in the doorway, holding a tray piled high with a breakfast large enough to feed an army. "I thought you'd never wake up," he went on, carrying the tray across to the bed.

"Is—is it still morning?" She managed to speak lightly, sitting up again and still clutching her sheet.

"Just barely." He placed the tray across her lap and sank down onto the bed beside her. "You look just like an angel when you sleep, did you know that?" He leaned over to kiss her briefly but very thoroughly.

Emerging from the kiss a bit breathless, she murmured, "Now I'm an angel. Did you watch me sleep?" There was something very disturbing about that thought.

"Of course I did." He smiled, picking up one of the two coffee cups on the tray. "I told you that I'd enjoy waking up beside you in the morning, honey, and I certainly did. I also promised to fix breakfast this morning and serve it to you in bed. You will observe that I am doing just that," he finished gravely.

"Oh. Thank you." She picked up the other coffee cup, feeling decidedly unsettled and not sure whether it was because he'd stayed or because she had thought he'd left.

"Casey?"

Determinedly, she avoided his searching gaze, knowing that the relief she felt was plainly apparent in her eyes, and unwilling to admit that she'd felt devastated at the possibility that he'd left without a word. Staring down at the food, she said brightly, "It looks great! But then, you said you were good with breakfast, if I remember." I'm babbling, she thought disgustedly, absolutely babbling! The man unnerves me completely.

"Casey, look at me." He took her chin in one hand, forcing her to meet his intent eyes. "You thought I'd run out on you, didn't you? Without a word."

She managed a tremulous smile. "Well . . . I don't have very much experience in these matters. How should I know what to expect?"

"These matters?" A teasing, mocking glint entered his eyes. "Care to explain what you mean by that?"

"You know what I mean." She pulled away from him and concentrated on her coffee, adding somewhat defensively, "Overnighters."

"An overnighter that's going to last a lifetime," he said calmly.

chapter 7

CASEY SENT HIM a small, uneasy look, and made a production out of tucking the sheet beneath her arms. "Don't say things like that."

He watched as she replaced her cup on the tray and picked up a fork. "Why not? We belong together; your body knows it even if your mind doesn't."

She stared down at the omelette on her plate. She had, she knew, made a commitment of sorts last night, but she was still far too wary to commit herself completely. Her heart told her that she could trust Storm not to hurt her . . . but she didn't trust her heart.

"Tell me something honestly, Casey. Now—in the sane light of day—do you want me?"

She couldn't lie to him. "Yes," she whispered.

He hugged her fiercely, nearly dislodging the tray in the process. "Thank you for admitting that much, at least, sweetheart," he murmured huskily. "Doesn't it tell you something?"

Breathless as always at his touch, she said unsteadily,

"It tells me that there's a—a strong physical attraction between us."

His lean face hardened as he drew away from her, and he placed a finger across her lips when she would have gone on. "Honey, don't make me angry by trying to tell me that there's nothing more between us than physical desire! I know better, and I think you do, too."

She stared at him, feeling rushed, carried along by a current she had no control over. "I need time," she breathed softly. "Everything's happening too fast. I don't know what I feel . . ."

"And I promised to give you time," he said apologetically, his face softening. He sighed. "Sorry, honey, I didn't mean to rush you. Now that I know you belong to me, I guess I can wait awhile to make it official."

Casey closed her mouth and then said with a snap, "That's good of you!" *Damn* the man! How could he be so sure of himself—so sure of her?

"I thought so." He was maddeningly unperturbed by her irritation. "Just be glad I'm a patient man."

Torn between amusement and exasperation, Casey shook her head and picked up the fork again. "Patient, huh? Is that what you were exhibiting so much of last night? Patience?"

"You're not *that* inexperienced, honey."

She felt a flush rise in her cheeks, and she hastily took a bite of omelette. It was being forcibly borne in on her that cute comments or sarcasm just didn't have any effect on this man. Sacrasm rolled right off his back, and cute comments were distressingly apt to be taken literally. What could a woman do?

"You know," he mused thoughtfully, leaning back on one elbow and studying her, "you've been completely natural with me from the very beginning. Have you realized that?"

Casey looked at him, lying back on her bed wearing only the trousers of his tuxedo, and had to admit that he had a point. She didn't feel the slightest embarrassment or shyness around him.

Well, she knew why, of course. But he didn't have to know. "I wish you'd help me eat this," she complained mildly.

He smiled faintly and reached over to pick up the second fork. "Okay, princess. Subject shelved . . . for now. But we'll get back to it eventually."

She had no doubt that they would, but they didn't get back to it that day. After breakfast, they shared an indecently long shower, which included a great deal of laughter and more than one lewd comment from Storm. Casey was still completely comfortable with him, although she found that his constant touching took a little getting used to when they were both undressed.

Wearing jeans and a casual pullover, Casey cleaned up in the kitchen while Storm shaved. She was a little worried about what he would expect of her after last night, and she silently brooded about it as she washed dishes.

Judging from some of his earlier remarks, he still wanted to marry her. But that was absurd, of course. He didn't even have a good reason for wanting marriage. He was possessive and domineering and cheerfully arrogant. And he was rushing her. She didn't want to make another mistake; the last one had hurt too much.

But she didn't want to give up the incredible physical attraction between them. She didn't want to give up the companionship and the shared laughter. She didn't want to give up this unfamiliar feeling of closeness with another human being.

And—dammit—she liked being called princess!

The bottom line was that she didn't want to give up the man she loved. But she was afraid of that love, afraid of committing herself totally to a man she barely knew. He seemed so sure of the fact that they belonged together . . . and she wasn't sure at all.

She couldn't marry him. Not until she was sure. Sure of her own feelings, sure that she could trust him. But would he wait for her to know her own mind?

He had a peculiar talent for getting his own way, she thought with a little smile. Small things, mostly. Like her hair. Aside from the party the night before, she'd been wearing it down ever since he'd commented on it that first day. Because he liked it that way.

And he'd neatly backed her into a corner by declaring that they were engaged. To one of her father's closest friends, no less. And she was even getting used to his possessiveness.

Her thoughts turned to the night before, and Casey's hands stilled in the sudsy water as she stared blindly out the window above the sink. Possessive? God, the word might well have been invented especially for him! But tender, too. And the things he said...

What other man would call her a witch and a princess, and then explain exactly what he meant? What other man could so totally and completely portray a man in love without once saying that all-important word? And what other man could she even begin to contemplate spending the rest of her life with?

"Penny for your thoughts, princess."

Casey drew her hands from the water and dried them slowly, turning a guarded gaze to the man leaning against the counter beside the sink. "They aren't worth that much," she told him lightly.

He was silent for a moment, then reached out to trail a finger down her cheek, letting his hand come to rest on her shoulder. "I said that I'd give you time, honey," he reminded her softly, uncannily reading her thoughts again. "But you have to make me a promise."

"What?" she asked warily, trying to ignore the thumb moving caressingly against her collarbone.

"Stop fighting me," he urged quietly. "Give me a fair

chance to show you that we belong together. That's all I ask, Casey."

Casey stared into the tawny eyes and nodded slowly. Time—that was what she needed. With time, she could forget the bitterness of Roger's betrayal. With time, she could learn to trust her instincts again.

"Good." He leaned over to kiss her lightly, then straightened. "Just one more thing, princess. No more seeing other men just to spite me, okay? My temper can't take that."

She allowed a smile to creep across her face. "That sounds more like a command than a request," she observed amusedly.

"And if it is?"

"It'll be like waving a red flag at a bull."

He chuckled. "Make it a request, then."

"In that case, I'll comply."

With a sigh, Storm muttered sardonically, "Something tells me I'm asking for trouble by hitching my fate to you, princess!"

"You're asking for trouble?" she muttered, thinking of the party the night before. "What can I say about a man who threw me over his shoulder like a caveman— in full view of thirty highly amused people? I haven't forgiven you for that, by the way."

He grinned. "You will one day. And, truth to tell, princess, I enjoyed myself too much to apologize for that!" When she only gave him a pained look, he went on cheerfully, "Right now, I plan to drive to my hotel so that I can get out of this damn tux. Then you and I are going exploring. Do you like carnivals? I noticed one setting up the other day."

"I'm ashamed to admit it, but I've never been to a carnival."

"Never?" There was astonishment mixed with mockery in his tawny eyes. "You've been missing *all* the good things in life, haven't you?"

Refusing to respond to that, she told him calmly, "You'd better go before that place where you rented the tux charges you for another day."

"It's no fun fishing with you," he complained in a woeful voice. "You just won't rise to the bait."

"Are you kidding?" Casey lifted a rueful brow at him. "I know when to keep my mouth shut. Usually, that is."

He laughed, then gave her a pat on the rear and headed for the front door. "Be ready in an hour, honey."

She was ready in the allotted time, electing to wear her jeans and casual top. She knew enough about carnivals to realize that a dress simply wouldn't be appropriate.

Waiting for Storm to arrive, she had time to reflect on her life, aware of the steadily growing dissatisfaction that had plagued her now for days. She *had* missed a great deal of life, she realized dimly. The whirlwind entrance of a storm in the shape of a man had awakened her to that fact. What she had missed, more than anything else, was sharing.

Her father had drummed into her head that a scientist observed rather than participated. And so she had. From the age of five, when a grave little girl lugged home a bag of rocks and insisted that her father explain what they were made of, Casey had taught herself to observe. And she had continued to observe all through school.

She had dated only enough to realize cynically that few men saw beneath the surface, or even tried to. She had come of age in a world where values were changing drastically and tradition was no more than a vaguely despised word. The roles of men and women were being challenged daily, resulting in confusion and hostility.

Burying her basic femininity beneath the layers of deeply ingrained ambition and determination, Casey had fought her way into a field dominated by men. Not to show the world that she was as good as any man, but to prove to her father that she was as good as the son he had wanted.

She had felt guilty in college for taking courses not directly related to the field she had chosen. But her interest and fascination with living things had been too strong to totally ignore. So she'd squeezed in courses in psychology, botany, the life sciences. But there had been little time to spare for them.

It hadn't been easy to measure up to her father's standards. He was not only highly respected, but also considered a leader in his field. A consultant to huge corporations and governments alike, he'd flown in and out of his daughter's life, pausing only long enough to critically assess her progress. And never favorably.

Always in his shadow, she'd learned to smilingly accept the congratulations whenever her father made some breakthrough in physics, found or developed a new energy source, or located oil or natural gas against all odds. She'd learned to ignore the comparisons between her ability and her father's.

And she had made a name for herself. But the years spent in classrooms and laboratories now seemed wasted ones. What had she really accomplished? Nothing worthwhile. She had trudged along stocially in her father's footsteps, stubbornly determined to be what he wanted her to be and ignoring the rebellious impulses that reared their heads from time to time.

Her own common sense told her that she had inherited more from the laughing mother she barely remembered than from the autocratic, analytically minded father who had raised her. But she had ignored that, too. Just as she had virtually ignored the implied sensuality of a face and body bequeathed to her by a mother noted for being a stunningly beautiful woman.

That had been just another cross to bear in her efforts to show her father that she was worthy of the Mallory name. Men had clustered around her until they were

driven off by her aloof, professional attitude. She had
flirted with some, casually aware that it was expected of
her, but she had never formed more than a shallow,
surface relationship.

And then, after twenty-seven years of denying her
own nature, she had met Roger Collins. Like the hero
of every girl's dreams, he was tall, dark, and handsome.
Charming, flatteringly attentive, he was completely different from the men she had known. And there had been
an air of mystery about him, which Casey had found
exciting. He never talked much about himself, except to
hint at a tour of duty in the Far East filled with lost
friends and constant dangers. That had touched something in Casey—that maternal, protective instinct all
women possessed.

It wasn't until much later that she found out the "dangers" in the Far East had included drug smuggling and
black marketeering, to mention only two of his shady
dealings in that war-torn land.

But she hadn't known that then. She had known only
that she had found him disturbingly attractive. Within a
matter of weeks, they had become engaged. Her father,
acting as a consultant to some European foundation, had
known nothing about it until the trouble started.

Even then, Casey had not suspected her fiancé. He
was certainly not a traitor!

Lacking the so-called "necessary academic qualifi-
cations," he had been unable to gain a position on the
project Casey was working on through the usual routes.
But Casey had been impressed by his self-taught exper-
tise in computer science, and she'd pulled a few strings
to smooth the way for him. She had used her name, for
the first time in her career, to get the proper security
clearances for him. And Roger had been hired.

For weeks, everything had gone well. As part of the
staff of computer experts, Roger had worked as tirelessly

as the rest in sorting and classifying data that came out of the lab.

Then documents began to disappear. The computer began to suffer memory lapses, and there was a small, unexplainable explosion in the lab, delaying vital work. Security was tightened, and Casey loyally vouched for Roger, putting her reputation on the line.

She believed in him. Only later did she begin to add up certain actions of his. His increasingly short temper, the moodiness, the tension. His anger whenever she elected to work late in the lab.

The doubts had begun creeping in then. She had been working long hours to complete the project—usually alone in the lab—and when she had begged off from a date one night, he had lost his temper and hit her. The next day brought a contrite apology, which Casey accepted.

Three days later, he was gone...and so was a vital report on the progress of a government-funded project.

The whole thing was kept quiet, but some news leaked out. Casey wanted to crawl away somewhere and hide from the pitying looks, the superior attitudes of the men on the project. Only the arrival of her father served to stiffen Casey's spine. But his public support became a scornful tirade when they were alone.

After it was over, and Casey had been proven innocent of everything except stupidity—her father's words—she left Virginia and took a long vacation, licking her wounds in private. Then she had come to Arkansas and gone to work for Apollo.

And for four months, she had very nearly buried herself in her work, painfully aware that whatever respect she might have gained in her father's eyes had been lost by a single, tragic mistake on her part. She wouldn't let that happen again.

Then came Storm.

He blew into her life like a particularly violent version of his namesake, knocking her off guard and off balance from his first words. He made her rage and laugh—often at the same time. He was dominating in a manner that just couldn't be fought, and utterly outrageous more often than not.

He seemed to read her mind with uncanny accuracy, apparently knowing her better than she knew herself. He said that she was ruthless. And intelligent and beautiful and passionate . . . and he seemed delighted by each trait. He said that they belonged together.

And last night, he had encouraged her passionate nature to emerge, had teased and tormented her until she had wanted nothing more than to belong to him. As if something inside of her had known that this man was her destined mate, the other half of herself, she had made herself vulnerable to him in a way that she would have not believed possible.

On some level she couldn't name, he had set her free. He had shown her a special closeness, a strange and magical sharing of self that was intoxicating . . . overwhelming . . . addicting.

She had no experience to relate it to. With no one else had she shared rage and humor and passion. And she wanted to share even more than that with Storm. She wanted to share a home filled with love and laughter. She wanted to share hopes and dreams and the little triumphs and failures that filled everyday life. She wanted to fall asleep in his arms and wake up in his arms, and hold his child to her breast.

But she didn't know how he felt—really felt—about her. He acted like a man in love. She couldn't trust her instincts to tell her how he felt; she was only just beginning to realize how she herself felt—never mind anyone else.

Her heart insisted that Storm was an honest and decent

man who would never betray her, never intentionally hurt her. But her heart was still wrapped in the misty glow of her newfound love, and couldn't be trusted to see clearly.

Three men had shaped her own image of herself, her ego. First had been her father, leading, pushing, prodding her to be something she wasn't. She had been driven by his will rather than her own, accepted his choices, obeyed his commands.

Then Roger had appeared, and all the bottled-up love inside her had been given to him. But he had flung it back in her face, leaving her shaken and alone and betrayed in the very worst way.

And now Storm. Intentionally or not, he was shaping her self-image more strongly than either of the men before him. He was showing her a side of herself she had never seen before—a humorous, passionate, feminine side of herself. Not leading or pushing her to see. *Letting* her see. And that made all the difference.

If only she could trust her heart.

Casey pushed her troubled thoughts and questions aside and simply enjoyed her day with Storm. He was the perfect companion, keeping her laughing and cheerful all afternoon.

They went to the carnival first, enjoying the sideshows and trying their hands at the games. Storm won most of the contests easily, displaying a born talent for throwing rings over milk bottles and darts at balloons. They had to make one trip back to the car just to deposit all his winnings, which included three stuffed pandas, a tasteful assortment of sham-Oriental fans, two peacock feathers in living color, and two sailor hats, one of which proclaimed "Foxy," the second one "I'm with Foxy." Casey refused to wear either one of them.

Storm laughed at her when she insisted that riding the

merry-go-round was a lifelong ambition, then he stood and grinned at her while she rode happily and ate cotton candy. She caught the brass ring.

They shared a seat on the Ferris wheel, which provided an eye-popping view of surrounding El Dorado, then they went through the haunted castle and listened to stereophonic screams and watched skeletons emerge from dark places. Storm dared her to try some of the more adventurous rides, then patently enjoyed the fact that she clutched at him through one hair-rising moment after another.

Intending to get even for his sadistic challenge, Casey dared him to try his strength. She had watched more than one husky specimen fail to ring the big brass bell, and she had already come to the conclusion that the thing was probably rigged. Storm hefted the large mallet and . . . rang the bell.

More resigned than admiring, Casey silently accepted a colorful stuffed dragon to add to what Storm had already referred to as *her* collection. "Thanks," she murmured in a voice that quivered in spite of all her efforts.

Storm grinned at her. "Want a canary? They're prizes over there at the shooting gallery."

Casey had seen them. *Live* canaries. "I have a cat," she pointed out calmly.

He took her hand and began leading her between the double rows of games and try-your-hand-at-whatever. "How about a feather boa?" he asked cheerfully.

She choked back a giggle. "No, thank you," she responded in a carefully polite voice. "They're not quite my style."

"Well, here's something that is," he pronounced with satisfaction, pulling her to a stop before yet another dart-and-balloon game.

Casey searched the prizes and realized immediately what he was after. He got it, too. But it took six tries, and the gamesman was beginning to look a little wild-eyed toward the end. So was Casey. Added to her dragon were a gaudy bead necklace, another peacock feather, a molting feather boa, another fan, and a revolting-looking kewpie doll. By the time Storm won the glittering crown, there was no place to put in except on her head.

"There you go, princess—now you're duly crowned."

Casey carefully spit out a stray feather from the boa and stared at him. "Thank you," she murmured faintly.

"Anything else you'd like?" He was rubbing his hands together and casting a measuring eye over the few remaining untried games.

She dropped the dragon and the fan to clutch at his arm. "No," she insisted hastily, "this is quite enough! Besides, if you win any more, the carnival will go broke."

"If you say so, sweetheart." He bent to pick up her fallen loot, then caught her hand and began leading her toward the entrance. "I think we've had enough, don't you? Besides, I have a surprise planned."

"What kind of surprise?" she asked warily as they were approaching the car.

"You'll see." Storm unlocked the car and helped her to stow the prizes in back. Once in the car, he drove toward a part of the city unfamiliar to Casey, finally ending up at a mostly deserted scenic park.

"More rides?" she quipped as he parked the car and came around to open her door.

"Nope." He stepped back to the trunk and opened it, producing a large wicker-covered cooler. "A picnic." He grinned and added, "Didn't you wonder why I went to such pains to park in the shade at the carnival? I wanted to make sure this stuff didn't spoil."

"A picnic?" Casey stared at him. "But it's nearly dark. And it's October!" she protested, secretly delighted by the idea.

"Good thing it's a warm October," he said philosophically, taking her arm to lead her along a path to the small lake. "We'll have an almost full moon, too."

It was a thoroughly enjoyable evening. They had the lake to themselves, spreading the blanket Storm had brought and feasting on chicken, potato salad, and fruit.

Casey stretched out on the blanket at last, feeling replete and lazy. "You pack everything back up," she groaned. "I don't think I can move. All that on top of the cotton candy!"

"Cotton candy isn't very filling," he observed with a laugh.

"It is if you eat enough of it," she pointed out sleepily, trying vainly to smother a yawn with one hand. "And there was a candy apple, too."

"Don't forget the popcorn," he reminded in a helpful spirit.

"Beast." She yawned again, then felt her sleepiness disappear as his head suddenly blotted out the stars above her.

"Do you know what I'd like to do right now?" he asked in a husky whisper.

She knew. The answer was in his shimmering golden eyes. And the shiver that coursed through her body had nothing to do with the cool night air.

"I'd like to make love to you. Here...under the stars," he murmured. "Would you like that, princess?"

"We—we'd be arrested," she said unsteadily.

"But would you like it?" he asked insistently.

Casey stared up at him, feeling her arms creep up around his neck of their own volition. "Yes," she whispered at last. "I'd like that very much."

He bent his head, his lips gently teasing hers apart. It was a slow, insidious assault on her senses, his tongue moving to caress the sensitive inner skin of her lips, his weight slowly bearing her down into the blanket.

Casey forgot that this was a public park, and probably patrolled at night. She forgot everything. This was the closeness she craved. And she'd been right—it was addictive. She was hooked on it, hooked on this man. Like a junkie, she craved him.

His hand moved slowly under her knit top, sliding up to warmly cup an already throbbing breast. A thumb moved in a lazy circle as his mouth plundered her own, taking and taking until she was dizzy and breathless.

Her own hands were far from still, moving over the rippling muscles of his back, her nails digging into the flannel shirt. She hated the barriers between them, moving restlessly beneath his weight in an effort to be closer to him.

There was something especially beautiful about lying there under the stars, inhaling the pungent scent of dry leaves, listening to the whispers of the lake lapping against the shore, touching the man she loved. Being touched by him. It was an experience to luxuriate in, to treasure. Desire built slowly into a painful yearning, flowing slowly through her limbs, heating her blood. Each sense seemed suddenly acute, vividly alive. She could hear the hoot of an owl in the distance, the melodic chirp of crickets nearby. The lips moving sensuously on hers tasted of wine and fruit. The flannel shirt was pleasantly rough beneath her fingers. The tangy scent of his body was a potent stimulant, the stars above her a magical inducement.

She moaned softly when his lips left hers to wander lazily down her throat, her fingers tangling in the thick copper hair. And then, suddenly, he was lifting himself away from her.

Casey's murmur of protest died in her throat as awareness of the surroundings came back to her. Silently, she helped to pack away the remains of their picnic, thinking ahead to when they would arrive at her house.

Of course they couldn't make love here in the park! That would be insane—not to mention potentially embarrassing. But once back at the house . . .

Both were silent on the drive back. Storm helped her carry the carnival prizes into the house, dumping the colorful assortment on a chair and then straightening to regard her thoughtfully as she stood by the couch.

"I don't want to leave you alone, honey," he told her huskily. "But I promised to give you time, and I mean to stand by that promise. I want you to be very sure of how you feel."

"You—you're leaving?" she asked incredulously.

He nodded decisively. "I'm leaving. I don't want you to marry me, princess, only because we happen to be good together in bed. I want a wife who knows her own mind. So I'll wait—as long as it takes."

Casey had a peculiarly displaced feeling that this scene had been played before. And it *had*. But that had been before last night. He had said nearly the same thing then.

"I'll pick you up in the morning," he said going on calmly. "No sense in both of us driving to work."

Unwilling to beg for a night of his company, Casey crossed her arms over her breasts and nodded. "All right," she muttered, hoping to heaven that her eyes weren't giving her away.

Heading for the door, he instructed firmly, "Lock the doors. I don't think your prowler will return, but don't take any unnecessary chances. Good night, princess."

"Good night."

Casey stared at the closed door until she heard the roar of the Ferrari, then she walked over and mechanically threw the lock. With the same robotlike care, she fed her cat and then let him out for a few minutes. She tidied the living room, neatly lining up her prizes on the couch and staring at them for a long moment, then headed for her room and got ready for bed.

If her thoughts could have been read, it would not have seemed possible that she was thinking of the man she loved. She came up with various impolite names in three different languages, then proceeded to weave complicated plots designed to get even with that maddening man. Oddly enough, all of the plots resulted in a mental image of Storm totally in her power . . . and in her bed.

Lying in bed in her darkened, silent bedroom, Casey reminded herself that she really couldn't complain. Storm was only giving her the time she kept insisting she wanted. She knew—and *he* knew—that he had only to take her in his arms and she would do whatever he asked. But he didn't want it that way.

He wanted her to agree to marry him with a clear head.

That was funny. Really funny. How was she supposed to acquire a clear head, when he was doing such a terrific job of confusing her? He had her so rattled, she admitted woefully to herself, that she rarely seemed to have a single lucid thought, let alone be clearheaded about anything.

But one thing she was sure of. She didn't want to make another mistake.

Never mind the ache in her body. Never mind the empty space in her bed. Never mind the aloneness . . .

chapter 8

MONDAY WAS A hectic day. Even though her lab was still out of commission, Casey decided that the backlog of work for her staff was just too heavy to wait for their facilities to be put back into working order. It took only a few minutes early that morning to find a rather small, unoccupied lab in her building that had been more or less abandoned because of its size. Apollo hadn't yet decided what to do with the space, so Casey took the decision out of their hands.

Within an hour, she had moved her staff into the area and had commandeered various pieces of portable equipment from several of the other lab supervisors—"commandeered" being the operative word.

She very nearly ran Storm down in the hall with one of the bulky pieces of machinery.

"What," he demanded, sidestepping hastily, "are you doing?"

Casey gave the rolling cart another lusty shove. "What

does it look like? I'm stealing this audio-visual equipment away from Sal while he isn't looking."

Storm lent a hand with the pushing. "Who's Sal? And why do you need audio-visual equipment?"

"Sal's the supervisor for the refining lab down the hall. And I don't need this, but Sal wouldn't lend me something I *did* need, so I hope he has a conniption when he finds this missing."

Storm digested the information. "That's mean."

"Isn't it, though?" Casey grabbed for the cart as it made an unscheduled right turn, and winced when it struck a door with a soft thud. "Damn. You pushed too hard," she told her henchman.

"Sorry." Storm got the cart back on track.

Casey gave him a faintly irritated look as they continued down the hall. After her somewhat sleepless night, she wasn't very happy with him. "And what have you been up to? I'm supposed to be your liaison, you know."

He shrugged lightly. "So far, there's nothing to report. I've been trying to track down the components of that timer, which means I've been on the phone all morning."

"No luck?"

"No luck."

Casey sighed, then directed Storm to a neatly labeled door down the hall. "Put it in here." She swung open the door.

"That's a storage room."

"I know that."

He wheeled the cart inside, then stepped back to watch Casey close the door before inquiring bemusedly, "Are you going to tell Sal where it is?"

"Only if he asks me. Nicely."

Leaving Storm standing in the hall with a bemused look on his face, Casey strolled on down the corridor to her makeshift lab.

She kept her staff busy for the entire morning, determined to make a dent in the backlog of work. Soil and rock samples were tested, tested again, and then verified. Information was filed, reports were written up. The shoulder-to-shoulder working conditions were a bit unsettling, and Casey had to deal firmly with more than one case of frayed tempers.

Storm took her to lunch and then spent a good hour peering over her shoulder in the lab. Casey finally hefted a good-sized rock and ran him out because he kept murmuring suggestive comments into her ear and she was having trouble concentrating. Her staff seemed to enjoy the sight of Storm cowering in mock terror of her lethal weapon and threatening look.

He took her out to dinner and then dancing that night, holding her in his arms and whispering wondrous things into her ear. Their steps matched perfectly, and, between the wine at dinner and the whispered endearments, Casey was literally floating by the time he took her home. She was brought rudely back to earth, however, when she was left at her door with a chaste kiss and a cheerful goodbye.

The same thing happened on Tuesday night.

By Wednesday afternoon, Casey had ruined three fingernails and was less than her normally even-tempered self. She had decided wrathfully that Storm was deliberately tormenting her and, short of seducing him, she didn't know what to do about the situation. She could agree to marry him, of course. But she wasn't quite desperate enough to take that incautious leap. Not yet, anyway.

The strain was definitely beginning to tell on her, though, and Storm demonstrated an awareness of that fact when he came up behind her as she stood in the main computer room glaring at a pile of hard-copy printouts and put his arms around her waist.

"How much longer are you going to keep me waiting, princess?" he murmured huskily, nuzzling her ear through the heavy fall of honey-colored hair.

Quite irrationally, Casey wished that she had worn her hair up that day. Trying to ignore the sudden weakness in her knees, she said irritably, "It was your idea to wait."

With a grin in his voice, he teased, "Strain getting to you, sweetheart?"

"Don't laugh at me, dammit!" she snapped, glad that they were alone in the room. "You know very well what you're doing to me. And you also know that I wouldn't be totally averse to . . . having an affair with you." Her voice dropped a bit uncertainly on the last words, and she turned suddenly in his loose embrace to stare up at him. "But you keep insisting on marriage. Why, Storm?"

The golden eyes were unreadable. "Because I want a wife, not a mistress. I'll be a vital part of your life, Casey, not just someone you share your bed with if you happen to be in the mood." Steel crept into his voice. "I want a commitment. I want to know that no other man has the right to know that passion inside you. I want you to trust me, Casey—and when you agree to marry me, I'll know that I have that trust."

"What about what *I* want?" she asked almost inaudibly, trying in vain to understand the gritty urgency in his voice.

He smiled oddly. "You can have whatever you want, Casey—if you're strong enough to fight for it. Brave enough to reach for what you want in spite of the fear that you may not get it."

What was he telling her, she wondered vaguely. That she could have his love only if she was capable of fighting for it? Fighting what? Or . . . whom?

He tilted her face up suddenly, searching her puzzled eyes intently. Then he shook his head regretfully. "I'm pushing again," he murmured. "Don't worry about it, honey—you'll figure it out on your own. I just hope it's soon!" He gave her a lusty slap on the rear, grinned cheerfully, and strolled out the door.

Rubbing the abused portion of her anatomy, Casey muttered darkly to herself and turned back to the print-outs, then flushed vividly as she saw Ham standing in the doorway of his connecting office.

"You know," he remarked thoughtfully, obviously having seen the swat, "I don't like that man. I really don't. But I have to admit that he has a certain . . . style." He grinned mockingly.

Without deigning to respond to that, Casey picked up the printouts, tucked them under her arm, and stalked back to her office. Needless to say, she was not very happy with mankind in general—and Storm in particular. Dropping cryptic remarks and then leaving her with the indignity of that swat! Damn the man!

Slamming the printouts down on her desk, she sank into her chair and reached for the phone as it began to ring. "Hello?"

"Casey?"

She forced herself to relax. "Hello, Dad," she murmured with a forced calm. "You're back early, aren't you?"

"I was called back," John Mallory told her in a cool, commanding voice she had listened to all her life. "I'm in Washington at the moment. Collins is back in the country," he announced abruptly.

Half expecting that, Casey nonetheless felt a shock. "Oh?"

"Did you know?"

Her lips tightening, she stared blindly across the room. "No," she told him evenly. "I didn't know. But I suspected."

"What's been happening there?" he demanded.

She didn't want to tell him, but she knew that she had no choice. If she didn't tell him, he'd just call up Porter and find out from him. "Trouble," she replied succinctly.

"The computer's been tampered with, and there was an explosion in the lab. The company's hired someone to . . . look into it."

There was a long silence from the other end of the line, and then he asked tersely, "Are you under suspicion?"

How to answer that? According to Storm—no. According to her own common sense—yes. "No more than anyone else," she finally replied, her voice steady.

"Do you think it's Collins?"

"I don't know." She hesitated, then went on. "A timer was found in the lab after the explosion. Once it's checked out, we may know more." Her lips quirked in self-mockery as she noted her own use of the plural "we."

"Just in case," her father muttered, "I'll pass along that information to certain . . . interested parties here. Collins won't get out of the country a second time." His voice was grim. "And you can expect me there within a couple of days."

"That isn't necessary, Dad." It took a supreme effort of will to keep her voice level.

"Isn't it?" He laughed harshly and then changed the subject abruptly. "I know that Apollo didn't call in a government investigator, so they must have hired a garden-variety troubleshooter. Who is he?"

Casey wanted to laugh hysterically at that description of Storm, but she sternly quelled the impulse. "Carmichael," she murmured. "Storm Carmichael."

"The name has a familiar ring," he said musingly.

More concerned about the distinct probablility of her father's coming to Arkansas than anything he might know about Storm, she said as cooly as she could manage, "Dad, you really don't have to come here; there's no point."

"I'll be there in a couple of days," he stated unequivocally, and he hung up before she could say anything more.

Casey replaced the receiver slowly and stared at the phone without seeing it. Terrific. Just great. The last thing she needed right now was her father's autocratic presence. The trouble in her professional life was bad enough; what he'd have to say about her supposed engagement, she didn't even want to think about.

"What is it, princess? What's wrong?"

He was standing in the doorway of her office, golden eyes warm and concerned, and Casey fought a momentary impulse to fling herself into his arms and beg him to take her away from all these wretched difficulties. She conquered the impulse by reminding herself wryly that he himself was the biggest difficulty.

"Dad just called. Roger's back in the country," she announced baldly.

Storm came slowly into the room, dropping into the visitor's chair, which groaned and nobly bore his weight once again. "Is that why you were looking so tired and miserable just now?"

Casey smiled in spite of herself and replied honestly, "No. I always suspected Roger of being nearby, and you know it. I'm just not particularly pleased by the fact that my father is flying in to watch over his erring daughter."

"Erring?" Storm lifted an inquiring eyebrow.

Her smile dying, Casey shrugged moodily. "Dad has the inescapable conviction that disaster will strike unless he's nearby," she muttered. "One of these days, he's going to realize that I'm a grown woman and perfectly capable of taking care of myself."

Storm smiled slightly, but his eyes were oddly watchful. "Why don't you tell him," he suggested calmly.

She shrugged again, feeling that irritating dissatisfaction inside of her. Unwilling to explore the feeling right now, she changed the subject abruptly. "Do you have any news on that timer? Your friend seems to be taking an awfully long time checking it out."

"It takes time." He lifted one shoulder in an apologetic

shrug. "Since we know Collins is in the country, it narrows the field considerably. You always suspected him."

"I thought I was just being paranoid, though." Casey sighed and tapped a finger restlessly against her desk top. She wondered vaguely if she should tell Storm about the peculiar feeling she'd had for the past few days of being watched, but she dismissed the thought. That *was* just being paranoid, she decided silently.

"Once burned, eh?" He smiled crookedly. "You were right in this case, though—at least about the possibility of Collins's being involved. Personally, I hope he shows up."

She felt a smile tugging at her lips. "So you can break his neck?" she inquired teasingly.

"Something like that."

"You'll have to get in line. Dad quite definitely had blood in his eye, and he mentioned that there were some people in Washington anxious to get their hands on him." There was a definite satisfaction in the image of Roger under siege, she thought to herself.

Storm laughed and got to his feet. "I have some calls to make, honey, so I'll meet you here at five."

She nodded and watched him leave the office, then sat back in her chair and brooded silently. Storm hadn't been surprised by the news that Roger had returned to the States, and for some reason that bothered her. He had told her very little about his investigation, which was annoying but not unnatural. Her status as his liaison was really a formality; she wasn't intended to get involved in his work unless some problems arose. But knowing very well the speed with which Storm moved, surely he'd made some progress in almost a week. Did he know for certain that Roger was involved?

But five o'clock, Casey knew. For sure.

She was standing by the window, staring stonily at a vase filled with roses that sat on her desk, when Storm entered her office. The delivery man had just left, and she hadn't touched the flowers.

"Ready, honey?" Storm asked cheerfully as he came in, then he halted and stared at the roses.

"You didn't send them." It wasn't a question.

"No." He regarded her over the top of the flowers. "Do you know who did? Is there a card?"

"No card." Casey met his searching gaze steadily. "But I know who sent them. Roger." She nodded toward the single white rose nestled among the red ones. "That's his trademark."

Without hesitation, Storm gathered the flowers and dumped them into the trash can by her desk. "Bastard," he muttered.

Casey didn't protest. She had had an uncharacteristically vicious urge to tear them into shreds herself. Quietly, she told Storm, "You can forget about narrowing the field, now. If Roger's in El Dorado, then he's in on whatever's going on, right up to his eyebrows. And he's in El Dorado."

Storm didn't respond to her statement until they were in the Ferrari and heading for her house. There was an unwanted frown on his lean face, and whatever his thoughts were, she realized silently, they were certainly grim ones.

"I don't want you in that house alone," he said suddenly, his voice flat. "Collins is after that timer, and, as far as he knows, you could be carrying it around in your purse." Turning the car into her drive, he added authoritatively. "We can get a room for you at my hotel, at least for a few days."

Carey's instinct was to obey him without question, but a surge of stubbornness was at the fore by the time they entered the house. She dropped her purse on the couch and turned to stare at him, ignoring his brisk command to pack a few things.

"I'm not leaving, Storm." Her voice was very firm. "I won't be driven out of my home, even temporarily. And most especially not by Roger."

"Casey, he's a dangerous man—"

"I have my gun," she interrupted calmly, "and I know how to handle it. If he breaks in here, I'll use it."

"Have you ever shot a man before?" he asked brutally.

"No. But I will if I have to," she said evenly.

He sighed impatiently. "Honey, I know you have the courage, but I don't want you going through that. And you said he knows judo: there's every chance that he could take the gun away from you before you could fire a shot."

"I'll take that chance."

"Well, I won't! You're coming to my hotel, princess, and that's final."

Casey shook her head stubbornly. "I won't. Storm, try to understand—I ran away from a situation Roger created once before; I'm not going to do that again."

"It's not the same this time!" He was clearly beginning to lose patience with her insistence. "You're not running away, you're just stepping out of his reach for a while."

Silently, she shook her head again.

Evidently realizing that issuing commands was going to get him exactly nowhere, he studied her thoughtfully for a moment, then said conversationally, "You know, I hope, that I'm going to do my best to talk you out of this?"

"I know." She was smiling ruefully.

He certainly tried. He took her out to dinner, where he argued forcefully throughout a three-course meal. Casey remained adamant. Changing his tactics, Storm took her dancing and spent the better part of two hours whispering endearments and gently wheedling.

Casey took an iron grip on her senses and emotions and firmly resisted. It was one of the hardest things she'd ever forced herself to do, and it gave her pause in her wistful thoughts of spending the rest of her life with this man. If she could barely resist him in this one small matter, what hope did she have of escaping total domination in a permanent relationship?

When they finally reached her house again, Storm came in without a word, and Casey wasn't terribly surprised. Torn between amusement and exasperation, she realized that he still had no intention of allowing her to stay there alone. But she faced him across the living room with an obstinate lift of her chin.

Taking due note of that fact, Storm glared at her for a full minute, and then a gleam of laughter lit his tawny gaze. "Made of stern stuff, aren't you?" he inquired with gruff admiration.

"I'm beginning to think so." She remembered his unscrupulous tactics on the dance floor, and her lips twisted wryly. If she could withstand that sort of persuasion, she was equal to anything!

"All right, then." He sighed. "I'll bunk down on your couch again, honey. You're not staying here alone."

Casey wondered vaguely if she had been hoping for this all night. But she was nonetheless startled to hear her voice suggest almost inaudibly, "There's a bed, you know."

He went very still, some emotion she didn't recognize leaping in the golden eyes. "Is that an invitation, honey?" he asked very quietly.

"Yes," she whispered, avoiding his intent gaze. "But . . ."

"No commitment?" he finished.

She nodded jerkily. "No commitment."

"Thanks—I'll pass." The words were flip to the point of insult, but his pained tone made Casey want to giggle.

"Well, don't say I never asked," she said spiritedly, and then hastily went to find a pillow and blanket when he looked at her warningly. There was, after all, such a thing as pushing too far.

She dumped the pillow and blanket onto the couch, politely requested that he put the cat out for a few minutes, and then bid him good night. She was halfway down the hall when she glanced back and saw him gazing after her with a look that nearly stopped her in her tracks.

Getting ready for bed, Casey thought indignantly that it just wasn't fair for the man to send her off to bed alone with that particular expression in his remarkable eyes. How was a woman supposed to think and behave sensibly when a man looked at her with such wistful longing?

And it didn't help that her body remembered only too well the night he had shown her what making love was all about. That memory, added to the fact that he had held her in his arms and danced with her a short time before, was not exactly conductive to restful sleep. Her bed felt even more empty than it had for the past three nights, and every time she closed her eyes, she saw a pair of tawny ones gazing down at her.

When she finally dozed off a couple of hours later, Casey didn't sleep deeply enough to have nightmares. But she woke abruptly, feeling uneasy and terribly alone. The moonlight was bright enough for her to see the clock on her nightstand, and she was vaguely surprised to see that it was only a little after two. She tried to go back to sleep, but that proved impossible. Both her body and her mind were too restless. She counted sheep but gave up at three hundred.

Face it, she told herself woefully, *you want him.*

It was not the best sleep-inducer, but it was a fact. And he was too near for her to ignore the fact. Without consciously deciding to do so, she found herself out of bed and silently pacing the floor. And she couldn't even summon the spirit to be disgusted with herself.

In a peculiarly dreamlike manner, she saw her hand reach for the doorknob and slowly open the door. She wouldn't let herself think about what she was doing. She'd think about it later. She'd probably hate herself later. But not now. For now, she just had to reassure herself that Storm was near. By a touch, perhaps. He was certainly asleep by now, and would never know about her shameless lack of willpower where he was concerned.

Reaching the end of the hall, she paused and stared toward the couch. It was impossible to see in the dim room, but Storm's stillness indicated sleep. Nonetheless, she hesitated. Pundit brushed against her ankles, and Casey nearly jumped out of her skin. She watched the cat head toward the kitchen, and wondered vaguely if there was any dry food in his bowl.

And then, without being conscious of movement, she found herself standing beside the couch and staring down at Storm's relaxed form. She stood there for a long moment, listening to his deep, even breathing and feeling an almost overwhelming urge to touch him. *He'll never know!* her mind kept insisting silently. *Just this once and he'll never know . . .*

It was a large couch, but Storm managed to occupy most of it. She sank down on the very edge, fascinated by the slow rise and fall of his muscular chest and the way the copper-gold hair gleamed. Slowly, her hand moved out to lightly touch the bare chest, feeling his heart beating steadily. She told herself that the single touch was enough. But it wasn't. Her fingers explored the lean ribs, the corded strength of his neck, then slipped beneath the low-riding blanket to touch his flat, hard stomach.

The first inkling she had of his wakeful state came when his hand suddenly snaked out to encircle her neck, and his stomach moved almost convulsively beneath her fingers.

"Storm . . . ?" she breathed huskily.

The golden eyes glittered up at her for a second, and then he was pulling her head down, his mouth unerringly finding hers. The scorching male demand and hunger in that kiss told Casey everything she wanted to know. He wouldn't send her back to bed alone.

She gave full rein to her own response, holding nothing back. Her lips moved on his, her tongue dueling eagerly with his own. She forgot everything except the craving inside her body and mind. Close to him . . . she had to be close to him again. That was the only thing that mattered.

Half turning, Storm somehow managed to gather her to him on the remaining space of the couch, thrusting aside the blanket until only the thin silk of her nightgown separated them. "Siren," he muttered, tearing his mouth away to explore the scented flesh of her throat. "Did you come in here to seduce me?"

"Don't be ridiculous," she murmured blissfully, instinctively turning her head so that he could reach the shiveringly sensitive area beneath her ear.

He groaned softly and shifted again on the couch, and Casey had to clutch at him to keep from falling off. With a throaty giggle, she suggested solemnly, "There's more room in my bed."

"You planned this," he accused hoarsely, but he lost very little time in rising from the couch and lifting her into his arms.

Not bothering to reply, Casey linked her arms around his neck and used her teeth to nibble delicately on his earlobe. She was only barely conscious that he was carrying her into the bedroom. Her deepest instincts told her that she belonged in this man's arms, and, for this night at least, she was trusting her instincts.

Storm lowered her gently to the green sheets and immediately followed her down, supporting his weight on his elbows as he slowly slid the straps of her nightgown down her arms. When she refused to unlock her arms from around his neck even long enough to dispense with the lacy straps, he laughed softly and snapped them.

Casey didn't protest; he would have pointed out that it was her own fault anyway. She lifted her head so that she could touch the tip of her tongue to the pulse beating rapidly at the base of his neck, feeling his hands smoothing the gown below her breasts.

"What you do to me," he groaned thickly, his eyes devouring the smooth fullness of her breasts, "should be against the law!"

"You know what they say," she murmured with a smothered laugh. "The best things in life are either illegal, immoral, or fattening!" The last word was gasped out as his mouth found the tip of one throbbing breast.

His tongue curled eagerly around the nipple his mouth held, as though the taste of her was something he had an insatiable hunger for. Moving from one breast to the other, he continued with gentle torment, his lips and teeth nibbling gently, his tongue stroking erotically.

Casey moaned raggedly, wondering dimly how she could have existed for twenty-eight years without knowing of this astonishing sensation. She knew, though, that it would never feel quite this way with any other man. She was Storm's woman, and for the first time, Casey had an inkling of just what that meant.

It meant that her body belonged to him on some elemental level. Her body . . . and perhaps something else. Perhaps her soul. Certainly her heart. There would never be another man for her. Not in this life. That was why she had this terrible craving to be close to him like this. He was her match, her mate. And, suddenly, Casey stopped fighting that.

And felt, oddly enough, stronger for the silent admission.

His hands continued to lower the nightgown slowly, his mouth following the path as it slid down her body. Casey felt his tongue tracing warm circles on her stomach, and then lower, to the soft mound below her belly. The nightgown was tossed aside, but she never noticed.

She gasped, her eyes wide and startled at the new, unexpected caress. Her nails dug into his shoulders unconsciously as red-hot waves of feeling washed over her and that shattering tension began to build.

"Please!" she panted breathlessly. "Oh, *please*, Storm!" Her body moved restlessly.

He moved slowly back up her body, stringing hot kisses over her flushed skin. "So warm," he rasped huskily, settling himself between her thighs. "So warm and sweet. Oh, *God*, I need you, Casey!"

She welcomed him eagerly, feeling a sudden fierce desire to trap him as he had trapped her, to hold him in her body and never let him go. It was a primitive, almost savage feeling, reflected in the supple strength of her arms as she locked them around his neck.

That strength, and the throaty little feminine growl which she uttered unconsciously, seemed to drive him to new heights of desire. He muttered encouragement as she began to move with him, their bodies reveling in their mating dance of grace and power and passion.

They climbed higher and higher, their appetite for each other taking them to the very brink of madness. Casey cried out hoarsely as he showed her, once again, that mystical, magical place of such enchantment, hearing her name torn harshly from his throat and feeling the shudder of his body answer her own.

It was a long time before Casey could even move. She felt drugged, utterly limp. As her body slowly cooled, she was conscious of a faint chill in the room, but she couldn't rouse herself enough to pull up the covers. Evidently, Storm felt the same.

"Be a good girl," he murmured, yawning, "and pull up the covers. It's the least you can do after so blantantly seducing me."

"I did no such thing." She couldn't even summon the energy to be decently indignant.

"Oh?" he murmured, mildly interested. "What would you call it?"

"I was walking in my sleep. Obviously."

"Liar."

She giggled weakly. "Who's in whose bed?"

"I was invited. I remember distinctly," he declared virtuously.

Casey twined several strands of red-gold hair around one finger and tugged slightly. "A gentleman wouldn't mention that."

"A gentleman," he stated firmly, "I never claimed to be. And I should spank you for making me go back on my word!"

"Did I do that?" she asked innocently, rubbing her cheek against his shoulder and feeling his arm tighten around her. "Funny, I don't remember dragging you down the hall."

He laughed deep in his chest. "I would have to be made of stone to resist your nighttime wanderings, honey, and you know it. I can barely keep my hands off you during the day!"

She smiled wonderingly at the desire he had never made the slightest effort to hide. "As I believe I've already remarked—you're a greedy man."

"I'm greedy?" He was wounded. "Who was walking in her sleep?"

Casey giggled and moved even closer to him. "If you tell anyone about that, I'll deny it," she warned.

"I don't kiss and tell," he responded with wounded dignity.

"No, you just throw people over your shoulder at formal parties," she countered pointedly.

"Are you still going on about that? It'll be something to tell our grandchildren. Pull up the covers, honey."

She sighed and then spent a moment tugging her hair from beneath his shoulder so that she could sit up and reach the covers. "I think I'll get this cut," she murmured almost to herself.

"No, you won't," he stated instantly. "When it reaches the ground, I'll hire a little boy to walk behind you and carry it, like a train."

Casey drew the covers up around them, laughing at the image his promise brought to mind. "That's absurd!"

He yawned, drawing her down to rest close beside him. "Well, you won't get it cut, anyway," he murmured.

She smiled as she felt his fingers moving in her hair and decided dimly that she'd keep her hair long after all. Relaxing against the warmth of his body, she also decided that she wasn't going to sleep alone again if she could help it.

Her last thought before sleep claimed her was that it was a good thing she'd told Porter that she was going to catch up on some paperwork at home tomorrow. It was doubtful that she'd have the energy to do anything else . . .

Several hours later, she half woke as he began to leave her, and she protested sleepily when she felt a draft of cold air replace his warm body. Then the covers were tucked around her carefully, and she barely heard his soft voice.

"I know you're not going in today, honey, but I have to. You go back to sleep."

She turned on her side and curled up like a sleepy kitten, her lips curving in a smile at his tender concern. Drowsily, she listened to the sounds of the shower running.

Even half asleep, it occurred to her that there was something very right about waking up with him. She had never felt so comfortable with another person.

He made her feel that way. He made her feel . . . safe. At home. Perhaps it was a part of that odd possession she had realized in his arms hours before. She was his woman. She could depend on him to take care of her. And that meant . . .

She wasn't alone anymore. Always, she had stood

apart from those around her. Observing. Not participating. Not sharing. On the outside looking in. Love, she had thought, would make her weak. But she had discovered a certain strength in giving up a part of herself to Storm.

But had he given a part of himself to her? She didn't know. He wanted her, needed her. She knew that. She didn't know how deeply his feelings for her went. He'd said that she could have whatever she wanted from him...if she was strong enough to take it.

She wanted his love. She thought that she was strong enough to fight for it—but was she brave enough to reach for it, knowing that it might be beyond reach?

Her sleepy mind grappled with the question. Courage. Storm said that she had it, but Casey wasn't sure. What was courage? The ability to grit one's teeth and fight for something? The ability to face what couldn't be faced, to get up after a fall and grimly keep on trying? The desire to grab at love with both hands and hold on wildly, because life was so short....?

Could she bear taking that chance again? Roger's betrayal had torn her up inside, but she knew with an awful certainty that if she fought for Storm's love and lost...it would destroy her.

"Go back to sleep, honey."

He was bending over the bed, his hair still damp from the shower. The golden eyes were glowing down at her, and Casey felt that she was lost somewhere in their depths.

"I have a lot to do today, so I probably won't be able to have lunch with you. I'll call you later this afternoon, okay?" He cupped her cheek in one warm hand.

Murmuring something inaudible, Casey turned her face until her lips were moving against his rough palm, her lashes lowered to hide the almost overwhelming love she felt for him. It was heart-stopping, the feeling she had for this man.

She heard him catch his breath oddly, and then he was bending to kiss her cheek lightly. "Sleep well, sweetheart."

Casey kept her eyes closed as she heard him move toward the door, opening them only when she was alone in the room. Had he whispered something else, she wondered. But no. It was just her imagination.

He hadn't breathed, "I love you."

chapter 9

CASEY SPENT THE day quietly. It took only a couple of hours to double-check the paperwork that was the result of her staff's extra effort during the past few days. That done, she studied several reports on the petroleum industry in general and wondered vaguely why Porter had asked her to read them.

Feeling energetic, she started cleaning the house, constantly routing Pundit from whatever spot he happened to be sleeping in, until the cat sullenly demanded to be let outside. Debi called to invite her to lunch, and she went willingly, only to be met by a knowing look the moment she walked in her friend's door.

"I noticed the Ferrari leaving without you this morning," Debi told her with a smile, "so I figured you'd be free for lunch."

"Where's the baby?" Casey asked calmly.

"Down for his nap, and stop avoiding the subject! When are you going to marry that man?" Debi demanded severely. "The glow in your eyes is positively indecent!"

Casey felt herself flush as she sat down at the small table in her friend's sunny kitchen. "Does it show so plainly?" she asked uneasily.

"If it was any plainer, it would be in neon!" Debi sobered, her brown eyes grave. "You're in love, Casey, and it shows. Why fight it? The man obviously adores you."

"Obviously," Casey muttered disbelievingly. "And just how did you glean that bit of information? Telepathy?"

Debi sniffed. "I knew it the first day, when he started ordering your around. A man only does that when he's in love. And a woman only lets him get away with it when *she's* in love."

Casey grinned in spite of herself. "So wise!" she mocked.

"Well, it's true!" Debi insisted.

With a sigh, Casey murmured, "That must be why I let him get away with it, then." And her tone was one of rueful admission.

"So, marry the man!"

"What makes you think he's asked me?"

"Has he?"

Casey hesitated. "Yes."

"Then what are you waiting for?"

"*Time!* Debi, I barely know the man!"

"You love him?"

"Yes, dammit."

"Well?" Debi grinned at her. "I don't think you have much of a choice, friend. Judging by the little I've seen of him, your Storm is going to get you to the altar even if you drag your heels all the way. Give in. Like the man said—it'll save wear and tear on your nerves, if nothing else!"

"You're a lot of help."

"Thank you."

An unwilling smile tugged at Casey's lips. "To be perfectly truthful," she murmured, "I've already decided

to take the plunge. It's just a matter of finding the nerve
for it."

"Close your eyes and jump," Debi advised cheerfully.

"Ummm." Casey lifted a brow. "But what if he's not
there to catch me?"

"Nothing ventured . . ."

"What is this—the neighborhood lonely-hearts col-
umn? I thought I came over here to eat."

"Temper, temper . . ."

Casey thought about her friend's words during the rest
of the afternoon. And her own. She *had* decided to "take
the plunge" and marry Storm—if he asked her again.
She was still afraid, though. It was a gut-level fear rather
than an intellectual one.

And she wondered if she had at last found the defi-
nition of courage.

If courage meant simply taking some kind of action
that was frightening, only because *not* taking action was
even more frightening, then she understood the meaning
of the word now.

She was afraid of what would happen—or wouldn't
happen—if she married Storm. But she was infinitely
more afraid of what would happen if she didn't marry
him. She'd lose him. He would be gone from her life,
leaving only the aching memory of sharing. Passion.
Companionship. Laughter.

Did he love her? She thought that perhaps he did. But
even if she thought he didn't love her, Casey was still
willing to marry him. Because they would still have the
passion and the companionship and the laughter. And
there was nothing at all wrong with that.

Having decided that, Casey felt strangely content. She
wondered if he would want children, and spent a dreamy
hour or two thinking up names for them. Whether he
liked it or not, she decided calmly, there would be two
children. Four? No, two. She wasn't getting any younger,

after all. Four would be unreasonable.

Would they live here in Arkansas? Maybe. It didn't really matter where. Not really. She'd follow him around the entire world in a wheelbarrow if he asked her to.

Grinning at that thought, Casey finished cleaning up the house and then baked a batch of cookies because she was in the mood. She fed one of them to Pundit and ate several herself, then cleaned up the mess she'd made in her enthusiasm.

When four o'clock arrived without a call from Storm, she began to wonder what was going on. She trusted him to take care of the mess at Apollo, but she wished he'd tell her more.

One thought led to another, and Casey wondered edgily how her father would take the news of her impending marriage. After Roger, he didn't think very highly of her judgment. She didn't really blame him for that. The mistake had nearly cost her a career, and it had taken a large chunk out of her self-respect.

But she was suddenly very tired of apologizing for that mistake. To herself and to everyone else.

It was time to get on with her life.

Her bitterness toward Roger was still present, but it wasn't as strong as it had once been. It wasn't a crippling bitterness anymore. She could deal with it now.

Odd, she mused silently, how much had changed since Storm had come into her life. Had it only been a week? She felt as though she'd known him for years!

The ringing of the telephone interrupted her musings, and she felt relief wash over her. It would be Storm, of course, telling her to ready in an hour, when he'd pick her up to go—wherever. Those cheerful demands were a part of his personality she loved . . . and was frustrated by.

"Hello?"

"Hi, Case."

Casey's fingers tightened around the receiver until the

knuckles were white, and she felt her stomach tighten. But her voice was perfectly calm—even casual—when she spoke to the man who had so nearly destroyed her career. "Hello, Roger. I heard you were back in the country. And I got your flowers."

"You heard?" The lazy drawl stiffened a bit. "How did you hear?"

"Dad. He called me yesterday. It seems that certain . . . parties . . . have been waiting for you to show up. Rather anxiously, in fact. I imagine they're all heading this way by now."

"Oh?" The normally attractive voice lowered to a cold, intimidating note. "A bit of revenge, honey? Have you been setting me up?"

Casey wondered vaguely why the word "honey" could sound like an endearment on one man's lips and an obscenity on another's. "Not at all," she replied sweetly. "I just happened to mention that Apollo's computer had been tampered with and a lab blown up—both specialities of yours, as I recall. Dad made the connection without any help from me."

Roger swore, and not softly. "And he called out the troops, huh? Your father's a very unforgiving man, sweetie."

"He just doesn't like to see the family name dragged through the mud. What do you want, Roger?" She was impatient.

"The timer." His voice became low and cajoling, shedding the savagery with the ease of a born charmer. "And I'm willing to deal for it, sweetie."

"Deal?" Casey allowed her voice to show interest, but her mind was working keenly. So Storm had been right: the timer would point to the culprit—and that culprit was Roger. "What makes you think I'd want to deal with you, Roger? You haven't exactly proven yourself to be trustworthy."

"You have a choice, sweetie." The very pleasantness

of his voice sent a chill down Casey's spine. "You can deal with me—or go to prison with me." He laughed softly. "Lover-boy wouldn't like that, would he?"

Casey ignored the question, knowing now that her feeling of having been watched for days had been correct. "Covering yourself again, Roger?" she asked quietly, feeling a rage such as she had never known.

"Had to, sweetie. In my little tiptoe through the computer, for instance, I left a few things that point to you. But the real clincher, Casey, my love, is the fact that another oil company just bought the exploitation rights to a site Apollo was considering—and your name's on the lab report verifying the samples."

"It's a forgery," she said tightly.

"Sure it is." He laughed. "But that'll take awhile to prove, and until then you'll be under suspicion again. And in this business, sweetie, it's only *two* strikes and you're out."

Her mind still working frantically, Casey asked slowly, "Then what is it you have to deal with?"

"The lab report. The company I work for has an independent report, but they saw the one I have, and that's the one that sold them. You have quite a reputation for thoroughness, honey." His voice hardened. "Now, either you exchange the timer for this report, or else I send the report to Apollo—and it's on the other company's letterhead. Your choice, sweetie."

"All right," she said evenly. "Where do I meet you?"

"My hotel."

"No way!" she snapped immediately. "Somewhere public, Roger. The more people, the better."

"You have a nasty, suspicious mind, sweetie! All right, then; you pick the place."

Casey debated briefly and then said firmly, "The Western Museum. There's a new exhibit, so the place should be crowded."

"All right. Half an hour, Casey. But you come alone,

and you damn sure better bring the timer." He hung up abruptly.

Casey cradled the receiver slowly. She didn't *have* the timer. But maybe she could fake her way through a meeting with Roger—at least long enough for the cavalry to arrive. She smiled tightly at that thought, then picked up the receiver again.

Storm would have a fit—and not a small one—when he found out about this, but Casey wasn't about to tell him before the fact. He'd insist on meeting Roger himself, and she didn't want that. This was something she had to do in order to regain the self-respect Roger's betrayal had cost her.

Porter answered on the second ring, his voice filled with pleased surprise. "Casey! I was just saying to—"

"Dr. Porter, I'm sorry, but I don't have much time," she interrupted, speaking rapidly. "I've found out who caused the explosion in the lab. I think that the timer Storm found will prove it, but we have to move fast— Roger has friends who can get him out of the country very quickly. I'm meeting him at the Western Museum in twenty-five minutes. Could you contact the authorities, please, and have them meet me there?"

"But—but Casey—" Porter stuttered.

"No uniforms and no sirens," she instructed efficiently. "If he sees anything suspicious, he'll run."

"But Casey!" Porter bleated desperately.

"I'll explain everything later, Dr. Porter, but for now, just call out the troops. 'Bye."

Hastily, she picked up her purse and keys and headed for the door. It took only fifteen minutes to drive to the museum; it was sheer luck that she didn't get stopped for speeding. She pulled up in front of the museum and parked, grateful to see that she'd been right about a crowd. She got out of her car and started up the broad walkway, vaguely noting the decorative shrubs and benches that gave the place a parklike air.

"You're early."

Whirling, her instinctive alarm was replaced by guardedness as she watched Roger stroll from behind one of the large shade trees. "I want to get this over with as soon as possible," she told him tightly. "And stay right where you are."

He halted, smiling faintly as he glanced toward the building a few yards away. "I don't think we have to go inside, do you?" he asked sardonically. "You should feel safe enough with all these people around."

"This is fine." She studied him, for the first time objectively, and wondered how she could ever have believed herself to be in love with him. He was handsome, certainly: tall and dark-haired, with a careless, charming smile. But she could see, now, the weakness in his face, the surly curve of his lips. And his eyes were hard. "Do you have the report?"

He patted his coat pocket, still smiling icily. "I have it. Do you have the timer?"

"Of course," she lied coolly. "But before we make this little switch, I'd like to ask you something. Why?"

"Why frame you, you mean?" He shrugged. "Why not? The first time I did it because you just happened to be working on a project I wanted access to. This time— well, let's just say it was for old time's sake. I had to have somebody to pin it on, after all."

Good Lord! And she had compared this—this *creature* to Storm? She needed to have her head examined! Casey shook her head slowly, staring at him. "You don't feel the slightest compunction, do you?"

"Not at all," he answered coldly. "And don't start preaching, honey. Just hand over the timer. I'll take another restful trip abroad, and you and lover-boy can live happily ever after."

Wistfully, she murmured, "I wish I could see you call him that to his face. Storm's already expressed a strong desire to break your neck."

"The timer, Case."

Staring at Roger, Casey had been conscious for some time of movement behind him, and now she sensed rather than saw two rather large men moving toward him in a casual flanking movement. The troops? Well, there was no time like the present to find out.

"Actually," she said calmly, ignoring the butterflies in her stomach, "I don't have the timer."

His face hardened, the savagery back full-force. "Cute, honey. Real cute. Who has it?"

"Storm."

He swore, and a wicked-looking gun suddenly appeared in his hand. "Well then, sweetie, we'll just find out how much your lover values you, won't we? Start moving toward the parking lot."

Obediently, Casey half turned, her knees going weak with relief when the two men abruptly converged on Roger. Some kind of judo chop sent the gun falling from nerveless fingers, and then they were holding him firmly, one of them saying something low and urgent into his ear.

Silently congratulating herself for having—she thought—carried the whole thing off pretty well, Casey nearly jumped out of her skin when she was suddenly whirled around, hard fingers biting into her shoulders.

"Just what the hell," Storm gritted with obvious restraint, "were you trying to prove, Casey?"

He was angry. Furious. And Casey knew without being told that none of her reasons for pulling this stunt were going to be satisfactory. "He was trying to frame me again, Storm!" she exclaimed, trying to justify her actions.

Storm gave her a little shake. "I told you that I wouldn't let him do that again, Casey! Dammit, why didn't you trust me to take care of it? If I hadn't had these men standing by at Porter's, we never would have gotten here in time!"

"Standing by?" She looked uncertain. "You mean, you knew it was Roger? And you were going to—"

"We were going to pick him up," Storm cut her off coldly. "As it was, we had to scramble just to get here in time to keep you from getting your silly head blown off! Do you, or do you not, realize that this is not a game for amateurs?"

"I *know* that, but—"

"Wait for me at your house," he instructed tersely. "I'll be along in a few minutes."

"What are you going to do?" she demanded suspiciously, mistrusting the hot glitter in his eyes.

"I'm going to have a little talk with your ex-fiancé," he replied flatly, the glitter increasing in intensity.

Worried, she said hurriedly. "Don't do anything rash—"

"Home!" he roared.

Opting for discretion over valor, Casey beat a hasty retreat to her car. The large men, she reasoned hopefully, would surely prevent Storm from killing Roger. And if *they* couldn't, then *she* certainly wouldn't stand a chance!

She drove home at her usual speed, feeling truly free for the first time in her life. Her bitterness toward Roger was gone, replaced by rueful gratitude. He had shown her clearly just how different were the man in her past and the man in her present. Storm would never betray her, never intentionally hurt her. She could trust him with her heart, with herself.

All this time, she had been fighting against her instincts, believing that she had loved Roger and so couldn't trust herself to love again. But she had never loved Roger! She had been in love with the idea of love, not the man. And now she knew that the instincts born in love—real love—were reliable ones.

Arriving home some minutes later, Casey parked her car and went into the house, wondering when Storm would come. Still bemused by her recent discovery, she put her hair up and took a shower, then pulled on a zip-up robe and went into the kitchen to fix herself a glass of iced tea. Pundit rattled the back door as she was heading toward the living room, and she paused to let him in.

The cat followed her to the couch and jumped up onto the coffee table, surveying her with his normal Oriental impassivity, and Casey felt her lips twitch. "Ready to become part of a family, cat?" she asked dryly. Pundit discovered a speck of dirt marring one velvety paw and busily repaired the minor flaw.

Casey grinned faintly. "I bet you've had your bags packed since the first day he walked through that door! You've been on his side all along, haven't you?" The unresponsive cat jumped down from the table and went to curl up on his favorite chair in the corner. Casey smiled resignedly. "Why do I bother talking to you?" she murmured. "You never answer me."

She heard a car door slam at that moment, and she hastily got to her feet, setting her glass on the end table. Oh, Lord, he was still angry! And, like his namesake, he'd probably express himself quite forcefully. She'd be lucky if he didn't turn her over his knee...

Storm didn't bother to knock. He simply came in, slammed the door, and then stood there glaring at her.

"Hi," she offered uneasily, cautiously putting a chair between them. "Everything all taken care of?"

"Everything but you," he responded ominously.

Casey studied him for a moment, then smiled slightly and murmured, "Well, before you light into me, you'd better go put some peroxide on those knuckles. They look a bit bruised."

Storm dismissed that with a wave from one slightly cut-up hand. "What were you trying to prove, Casey? Just tell me that!"

Knowing that he was too angry to accept anything she might tell him right now, Casey remained mute, staring at him.

Storm made up for her lack of conversation. Easily.

"We're all set to leave Porter's house and pick up Collins, and then you call, and before Porter can get a word in, you're gone—to meet Collins!" His voice was just a shade softer than thunder. "We *know* he's armed...*and* desperate to get his hands on that timer...*and* has a track record that proves he doesn't flinch at using violence to get what he wants! And *you're* going to meet him!

"I have never been so furious in my life!" he continued, in a voice that amply confirmed his statement, beginning to pace around the room. "You need a keeper—do you know that? And you're going to *have* one, dammit! Me!"

Casey thought about interrupting his tirade but decided to let him rage on. At least now she knew that he wasn't a man who struck out in a temper. She thought of some of her own rages, and fought to hide a smile. Life was not going to be dull!

He stalked over suddenly, gripping her shoulders roughly. "No more games! I'll give you plenty of time to learn to trust me, Casey, but that time will be spent as my wife! We're getting married Monday afternoon at four o'clock! Understand?" he demanded in a modified roar.

Casey opened her mouth to speak, but she was prevented by the shrill summons of the doorbell.

Swearing violently, Storm marched over to fling open the door. "Well?" he barked. "What do you want?"

The distinguished-looking older man on the front porch glared back, his deep-set green eyes blazing directly into Storm's. "To see my daughter!" he snapped, his voice every bit as commanding and not a whit less intimidating.

There are going to be some dandy fights between these

two, Casey thought with faint amusement, ducking under Storm's arm to stare calmly at her father. "Hi, Dad. Come in."

He stalked past the couple in the doorway, and Casey murmured introductions as she and Storm followed him into the living room. She was even more amused to note that neither man offered to shake hands, and were regarding one another with definite hostility. Oh, Lord—caught between two domineering men!

Ignoring her invitation to sit down, John Mallory took in Casey's robe and Storm's position as he leaned casually against the back of her chair, and asked caustically, "Did I interrupt something?"

"Not at all," Casey replied coolly. "Storm was just reading me the riot act; he can finish later." She heard Storm muttering something indistinguishable, but she ignored him. "Have you talked to Porter, Dad? You'll be glad to hear that Roger's behind bars."

Satisfaction flickered briefly in the green eyes so like her own, but the elder Mallory wasn't to be detoured so easily. "I've talked to Porter since I talked to you," he said ominously. "What's this about another engagement?"

"A *last* engagement," Storm injected firmly.

He was ignored. "Casey, you aren't serious? Didn't you learn anything from that fiasco with Collins?"

"I'm not Collins, Dr. Mallory," Storm pointed out with steel in his voice.

"I know exactly what you are, Carmichael." The older man's voice was cold. "You're a maverick, a man who sells his . . . services . . . to the highest bidder. Does Casey know, I wonder, about that revolution you participated in a few years ago?"

Casey could feel Storm stiffen behind her, but she said nothing. Staring at her father, she wondered dimly when he was going to admit that his daughter was an adult who would make her own decisions. She had made one mistake, certainly, but she wasn't making one now. No matter what her father said, no matter what dirt he managed to dredge up from Storm's past, she would not be swayed. Storm was an honest and decent man; she knew that as surely as she knew her own name.

"I'm not going to defend myself to you," Storm was declaring tautly. "If Casey wants to hear the story, then I'll tell her, but I don't think she'll ask. She knows what kind of man I am."

"I won't let my daughter make another tragic mistake!"

"Then let her make her own decisions!"

"And have a repeat of the Virginia episode?" Mallory laughed harshly. "I don't know what you're after, Carmichael, but since my daughter seems to have no common sense where men are concerned, I'll make this decision for her! There will be no marriage!"

"I don't need your permission, Dad," Casey said very quietly, suddenly tired of being spoken to as if she weren't even in the room.

"Casey, use your head!" Her father's voice was as commanding as it had ever been. "If nothing else, this man's a rolling stone! He's on the move ten months out of the year; what kind of marriage would that be? Will you give up your career and follow him around, or do you simply believe that an absent husband is the best way to avoid the responsibilities of marriage?"

Casey rose to her feet slowly, standing up to her father in a confrontation that should have taken place years before. "However I choose to conduct my marriage, Dad, is no concern of yours. I've listened to you all my life, tried to be what you wanted me to be. I chose a predominantly male field for my career just to prove to you—and maybe myself—that I was every bit as good as the son you had wanted."

She squared her shoulders, meeting the thoughtful stare of her father and only dimly aware that she had the

full and undivided attention of both men. "Well, I'm
tired of trying to be something I'm not, Dad! I've spent
half my life in classrooms and sterile labs, and what I
don't know about human relationships would fill text-
books! I'm tired of looking at rocks instead of people;
I'm tired of white coats and chemicals and microscopes;
I'm tired of worrying about classified documents and
security clearances; I'm tired of moving constantly in
your shadow! But most of all," she finished with a deep
breath, "I'm tired of trying to prove to you that I'm
worthy of your love and respect!"

If her earlier confrontation with Roger had freed her
from the bitterness of his betrayal, then this one was
freeing her from something far deeper and more basic.
And she felt exhilarated.

Too wrapped up in her newfound freedom to really
notice her father's uncharacteristic silence, she went on
very quietly, "I'm a grown woman, Dad—please accept
that. From now on, I'll make my own decisions. I'll
make mistakes, sure, but they'll be my own mistakes."

"And your career?" he questioned with unusual peace-
ableness.

"What's a career?" She shrugged slightly, a small
ironic twist to her lips. "It was never really my career,
anyway: it was supposed to be your son's. If I'd had a
brother, he would have spent his life butting heads with
you . . . and I probably would have been sent to the best
finishing schools in the world." She shrugged again. "I
think I'll try my hand at something for a while. Not
because of you or Storm, but because of me. You see,
Dad, I never really knew who Casey Mallory was—only
who she was supposed to be. I think I'd like to get to
know her now. I think I'll like her now."

Her father glanced past her shoulder at Storm for a
moment, then met her eyes again. "And does getting to
know yourself include marrying this man?" he asked in
a very calm voice. "A man you've known barely a week?"

Without looking at him, Casey asked quietly, "Storm, did you mean what you said just before my father arrived?"

"I meant it, princess," he answered immediately, his voice oddly husky.

Replying to her father's question, she said firmly, "Yes. I'm going to marry him. Monday afternoon at four. I'd like for you to be there."

"And if I'm not?"

"Then you'll miss your daughter's wedding."

Surprisingly—to Casey, anyway—John Mallory's stern mouth moved to form a faint smile. Shifting his gaze to Storm once more, he asked sternly, "Do you know what you'll be getting, young man?"

"I know." Storm's velvet-and-steel voice was deep and calm.

She half turned to look from one to the other, realizing that the hostility between the two men had vanished, but not sure why. She could sense that something was taking place here, that the two men in her life had somehow found a common ground. They suddenly seemed to understand each other.

"She's a strong woman," her father said astonishingly. "And once she discovers just how strong she really is . . ."

Storm smiled crookedly. "I know. It'll be a lifelong battle—and I wouldn't have it any other way."

"Brave man," the elder Mallory said with a peculiar smile. "Her mother was just the same."

Frustrated, Casey snapped, "Will you two please stop throwing cryptic comments all over the place and tell me what you're talking about?"

"You'll find out one day, honey." The casual endearment staggered Casey, coming from her father, and she was even more stunned when he crossed to hug her and lightly kiss her cheek. "I'll be staying with the Porters," he said over his shoulder as he headed for the door.

"Give me a call about the wedding."

Casey watched until the door closed behind him, then mumbled blankly, "He's never done that before."

"You've never stood up to him before, have you?" Storm asked softly, moving to stand before her.

She stared up at him. "No. But . . . I never expected him to take it that way. He's always been so . . . autocratic."

"To his child, certainly," Storm murmured, smiling down at her. "But his child just became a woman. She asked—no, *demanded*—that she be allowed to make her own mistakes, her own decisions. She demanded the right to take responsibility for her own actions. That's what makes an adult, princess. Not years, or experiences, but simply the desire to be responsible for oneself."

Casey frowned slightly, then asked, "But what was that last bit all about?"

Still smiling, Storm put his arms around her loosely. "Just that you're a very strong lady, with a power all your own. The power of strength and determination . . . and witchcraft."

She had a feeling that he wasn't really answering her question, but decided to let it pass. It didn't seem terribly important right now.

"I have a question, sweetheart." The golden eyes were suddenly very intense as he stared down at her. "Was that just a bit of rebellion staged for your father's benefit?" he asked huskily. "Or are you really going to marry me?"

"If you really want me," she whispered.

"*Want* you?" His voice was filled with a savage quietness. "Honey, I want you so badly that I ache with it."

"Right now?" she teased, suddenly needing him desperately.

"Any time. *All* the time!" Storm swung her up in his arms and headed for the bedroom.

Just before they reached the hall, Casey looked back

over his shoulder to see Pundit, still curled up in his chair. And as she met the China blue gaze, Casey saw one of her cat's eyes close in a slow wink.

chapter 10

"I DIDN'T GET a moment alone with you all weekend," Storm complained on Monday night as soon as the door closed behind the porter.

Tearing her gaze away from the beautiful sight of a full moon shining over the Pacific, Casey half turned from the window to smile at her husband. "Who's fault was that?" she asked pointedly. "You were the one who decided we had to be married early this morning so that we could fly to Hawaii for a honeymoon. And after Dad took a hand in the arrangements, it's a miracle we were married at all!"

Storm chuckled softly. "He did seem a bit disappointed when we had to whittle down his guest list."

"Whittle down?" Casey turned back to the window, smiling as she felt his arms slip around her waist. "How many people can you fit into a judge's chambers, for heaven's sake? His list could have filled an enormous cathedral and an entire city block! I heard you arguing with him, by the way, about that Nobel Prize winner he wanted to invite."

"It would have taken the man a week just to get to Arkansas," Storm declared calmly. "I wasn't about to wait that long." He lifted her left hand and planted a possessive kiss just above the wedding band and emerald engagement ring. Going on complacently, he said, "Luckily, I managed to convince him of the urgency of the situation."

"You didn't tell him I was pregnant, I hope?" Her voice was dryly amused.

"No." His arms tightened slightly. "I've been meaning to ask you, though, if you had..."

"Taken any precautions?" she supplied laughingly when his voice trailed away. "Nope." She tipped her head back against his chest and added definitively, "Things have been happening rather fast, you may remember. Two weeks ago, I was happily enjoying a calm and well-ordered existence."

"Happily enjoying?" He laughed softly. "You have to admit, princess, that life is much more exciting now!"

"Oh, is *that* what you call it?" she asked politely. "Within ten minutes, I decided that I was caught in the eye of a hurricane. I suppose some people would think of that as exciting."

"How about me?" he countered in a woeful voice. "I've had to deal with a stubborn, willful, unreasonable female who just wouldn't admit that I knew what was best for her."

In a meditative tone, Casey remarked, "I should have slipped the judge twenty bucks to put an escape clause in the vows."

"I would have slipped him fifty to leave it out."

Casey bit her lip and firmly changed the subject. "Don't you think it's time you told me what Roger was up to this time? And what *you* were up to?"

"I wasn't up to anything, honey," he said calmly.

"Don't give me that!" Casey turned to stare up at him assessingly. "I told you on Wednesday afternoon that Roger was in the country, and by Thursday you had men 'standing by' at Porter's. You knew long before that day he was in El Dorado, didn't you?"

"Well, his fingerprints were on the inside of the timer, you see," Storm explained gravely.

"What? Why didn't you tell me?" she demanded, unsure whether to be angry because of his silence.

"I didn't want to worry you," he said, disarming her immediately. "There was nothing you could have done about it, anyway. The local police had a man watching your house after the break-in, just in case, so—"

"Watching my house?" She stared at him, realization dawning in her brain. "Then, when you made all that fuss about my staying by myself Wednesday night . . ."

"Yes?" He was smiling.

Casey didn't know whether to swear or laugh. "You weren't the slightest bit worried! You just wanted to—to—"

"To be with you," he finished with a chuckle. "I figured you'd refuse to leave your house, sweetheart. So, of course, I had to stay there with you. After that, I crossed my fingers and hoped."

"And you have the nerve to accuse me of seduction," she marveled. "The *nerve!*"

"I thought it was rather a neat way of getting myself out of the promise I made to you. After all, I could hardly be expected to resist when you decided to seduce me . . . now, could I?"

"You certainly weren't resisting too hard!" she retorted spiritedly.

"Are you kidding? For the first time, you'd made a move toward me of your own free will; I wasn't about to fight that! And when you came creeping into the living room—"

"Enough about that!" she interrupted strongly.

He grinned. "Okay, princess—but I'll remind you from time to time!"

"I have no doubt," she muttered, thinking that a grown woman—and a married one at that!—shouldn't blush at the slightest provocation. "Now let's get back on track for a minute. What was Roger up to? As near as I could make out, he sabotaged the lab so that we couldn't complete the report on one of the sites Apollo was considering. Was he hired by another company or just freelancing?"

"Hired," Storm replied tersely. "A small company—wildcatters, really. Collins was promised a percentage of the profits if he found them a surefire prospect. Whatever he made by selling those documents from the Virginia project apparently didn't last very long; he needed the money.

"By the way—" Storm laughed suddenly. "Collins was sporting a beautiful set of battle scars from his encounter with Pundit! He was working alone through this, and he took a chance by breaking into your house. From what I gathered, he was hoping that you'd gotten rid of the cat."

"Pundit never liked him." She laughed suddenly. "I should have run like a thief when he conceived an immediate fondness for you! He was on your side all along."

"Of course he was." Storm was utterly calm. "Didn't anybody ever tell you that animals are terrific judges of character?"

Casey smothered another giggle. "I hope Dad doesn't know that. Did you see him and Pundit eyeing each other when we left? A definite personality conflict there!"

"They'll survive. At least for a couple of weeks."

"If you say so."

"I do." Seemingly awed, he added, "Your father unbent so much over the weekend that he can probably take even hostile cats in stride."

"He did unbend, didn't he?" Casey's eyes glowed

suddenly. "We spent all Friday afternoon talking, while you were getting everything wrapped up at Apollo. He told me about my mother, Storm—and she's been a forbidden subject all my life." She hesitated, then added softly, "He really loved her."

"I know." His arms tightened around her. "I knew that on Thursday, when he said that your mother was a strong woman. He respects strength, princess. The kind of strength you showed when you stood up to him for the first time."

"Thank you," she said quietly.

He looked surprised. "For what?"

"For showing me that I had that strength." Her smile was a little twisted. "I never knew that, Storm. Until you came along, I'd always considered myself weak."

"Oh, you're not weak, princess—far from it." He smiled crookedly. "As a matter of fact, when you discover the full extent of your strength, I'm really going to have my hands full! I'll probably want to turn you over my knee at least once a week!"

"What's that supposed to mean?" she demanded suspiciously.

The tiger eyes laughed down at her. "It means that you're a fighter, princess. You'll fight me for the sheer joy of it. And I'll fight you—until you use the one weapon I have no defense against."

"What weapon?"

He lifted a mocking eyebrow. "Oh, no! I'm not about to tell you that, my dear wife. My ego demands that I win at least a few of the earlier battles!"

A militant spirit entered her heart. "Battle number one is going to commence shortly unless—"

He lowered his head abruptly, using a weapon of his own, which was totally unfair and utterly successful.

Emerging breathlessly from the kiss, Casey had no trouble at all in reading the gleam that appeared in the tawny eyes. But there was one last thing she wanted settled. "Um . . . before I forget," she muttered haltingly, "Roger told me that he'd left evidence in the computer that pointed to me. Did you find it?"

"The second day."

"But you didn't suspect me?"

"No. I told you that. I also told you that I wouldn't let anyone incriminate you again. But you didn't believe that, either, did you, princess?"

She stared up at him earnestly. "That wasn't why I went to meet Roger, Storm. It was . . . a matter of pride. Self-respect. And I didn't know you'd already located him."

"Just don't pull another stunt like that one," he requested wryly. "It took a good ten years off my life to find out that you were going to meet that bastard."

Casey hesitated, then said slowly, "I'm not sure I want the answer, but I guess I have to know anyway. Did Roger have someone on the inside this time?"

"No, he was working solo." Apparently realizing that she needed all the answers so that she could put the entire matter out of her mind, he went on. "That Virginia project you were working on was government-sponsored, and so the security was pretty tight. Collins needed your backing to get inside the place. Apollo, on the other hand, is just another company with average security. With his cunning, he had no trouble at all getting past the guards and into the building."

"Then why did he set those explosions—here and in Virginia? And why did he leave evidence both times pointing to me?"

"The explosions were delaying factors and diversions. They stopped or slowed down work and kept everybody rattled. And Collins left evidence pointing to you to throw suspicion off himself and to give him time to get away clean." Storm shrugged. "He was just planning for the future."

Casey considered the information, then filed it away

in her mind. It was time for other things. "Speaking of futures—we haven't had a chance to discuss ours, you know. Dad asked me if we were going to be nomads, and I didn't know how to answer him."

"Nomads?" Storm lifted a thoughtful brow. "I'm a little tired of traveling, myself. How about you?"

"I wouldn't mind putting down a few roots." She looked at him curiously. "What did you have in mind?"

Storm grinned faintly. "With the ups and downs of the oil business, the board at Apollo decided that the company needs a troubleshooter on the payroll permanently."

"And?" she queried, trying to interpret the sparkle in his eyes.

"They offered me the job."

"And?" she repeated impatiently.

"I told them I'd check with my better half and get back to them.

"Storm!"

He chuckled at her exasperated tone. "I did. A lot depends on your career plans, you know. You were rather adamant to your father about not being particularly pleased with your career to date."

Ignoring, for the moment, his reluctance to state his decision—she knew very well that he'd made up his mind!—she said reflectively, "I'm not sure it would be a good idea for both of us to work for the same company."

"Separate buildings," he pointed out with an absurdly hopeful expression.

"Actually, we'd be in the same building," she murmured. "Or isn't troubleshooting considered administrative work?"

"So I've been told." He nodded. "The official title is Operations Coordinator." He lifted a quizzical brow as her comment apparently sank in. "Are you trying—in a roundabout way—to tell me something? Has Porter booted you upstairs?"

"He just appreciates my true worth," she informed her love in a wounded voice, then relented at his threatening look. "As a matter of fact, he did. When I told him that I wasn't happy staring at rocks in a lab, he asked me how I felt about supervising personnel and projects overall. He said that he didn't want to lose my knowledge and experience. Isn't that flattering? Anyway, I said I'd let him know."

Storm appeared to consider the situation. "I noticed quite a few nice houses in and around El Dorado. And we both like the area. What do you say we buy a house and put down roots there?"

"Judging by your clothes," she teased, "and with the price of real estate these days, I'm not sure we can afford it!"

He laughed. "Troubleshooting—as you've remarked —pays very well, princess. I have some money stuck in a bank in Texas; until now, I didn't have anybody to spend it on. I think we can afford a house." Almost as an afterthought, he added, "And the school system is great, so I hear."

"School system?" she murmured innocently.

"Sure." He was smiling, but Casey sensed an odd tension in him.

Casey traced a thoughtful finger down his lapel. "Now, that's something to think about," she said calmly. "I told Dad that I wanted to try something different. How good do you think I'd be at juggling a career . . . and a family?"

"Casey?" His voice was suddenly thick, impeded. "That's . . . the ultimate commitment."

"I know." It was barely a whisper.

His hands turned her face up with rough, tender urgency. "Casey? Are you willing to have my child?"

"Willing?" She swallowed hard as she saw the undisguised hope leaping in his golden eyes. "I'm more than willing."

"Why?" he pleaded huskily. "Tell me why!"

She smiled at him slowly. Taking the plunge. Grabbing at love with both hands, because life was so short. "Because I love you," she told him softly.

"Oh, my love!" He drew her fiercely into his arms, holding her tightly, his voice rough and shaken. "I was afraid I'd rushed you, that I should have given you more time! But I was so desperate for your love, Casey. I knew the moment I walked into your office that you were the woman I'd waited for all my life!"

She lifted her head, staring at him wonderingly. "You love me? Really love me?"

"God, yes!" He laughed unsteadily. "You can't doubt it, surely? I started telling you I loved you ten minutes after we met—and I've been telling you ever since."

"I suppose a woman just has to hear it put in so many words," she teased gently.

He framed her face with hands that trembled slightly, the tawny eyes devouring her love-drenched expression. "How could I help but fall in love with my Amazon princess?" he rasped hoarsely. "There she stood: tall, strong, unbelievably beautiful. With a spark of temper in her green eyes and music in her voice."

Casey felt her heart stop for a moment and then begin to beat madly. "I knew," she murmured throatily, "even then that you were going to be important in my life. But I was afraid. I didn't want to be hurt. So I fought my feelings."

Wanting to convince him of the depth of her love, she went on huskily. "I knew for sure the night of the party. And when we made love...oh, darling, I wish I could tell you what that meant to me! That closeness. I've never felt as close to anyone as I do to you. It's like...you're the other half of me, and I've found you after all these years!"

Groaning softly, he bent his head to kiss her with shattering tenderness. "My life," he whispered. "I felt the same. I don't know how I existed without you!"

Casey slid her arms up around his neck, molding her body to his and feeling his instant response. The feelings inside her, more powerful than she would have believed possible, threatened to burst their fragile human container. "I love you, Storm!"

"And I love you, sweetheart," he grated fiercely, sweeping her up into his arms with that astonishing strength and carrying her across the room to the huge bed. "Something I intend to go on saying to you and proving to you all the days of our lives!"

He undressed her slowly, tenderly, dropping warm, possessive kisses on each area of creamy flesh as it was bared. He seemed almost to worship her body, caressing her with a yearning, gentle passion that brought tears to Casey's eyes.

With his hoarse encouragement, she undressed him as well, delighting in this new experience. Knowing, now, how to please him, she used her hands and lips to tease and explore. She wanted to give him the same pleasure he gave her, to feel his body cry out to her for satisfaction.

With the ease of a man comfortable and sure of his own masculinity, Storm rolled over onto his back, allowing her to do as she would. As if it were the first time, she explored his body slowly, using a butterfly-soft touch. With instincts as old as woman herself, she tormented gently, teasing and yet not allowing him to take. There was a need driving her, a need to imprint every inch of his body on her mind for all time.

And then green eyes clashed with gold suddenly, and both knew that the playing was done. The room swung crazily as Storm assumed the master's role again, settling himself between her thighs with a peculiarly lionlike growl.

Casey clung to him fiercely, moving with him, astonished as always at the feelings building inside of her. She wondered dimly if the rest of the world knew of these incredible sensations, or if it were a secret shared by her and Storm. And then the wild, whirling tension gripped her mind and senses, and she forgot to think.

The tension built slowly, rising in them like an inexorable tide, until they were riding the crest of the wave together, crying out each other's names when the wave burst upon the shore. . . .

Utterly relaxed and content, Casey nonetheless sensed a lingering tension in Storm. She rolled over suddenly, and rested her chin on the hands folded atop his chest. "What is it?" she asked directly.

His golden eyes were sober. "You haven't asked me about that revolution your father mentioned."

"And I'm not going to," she responded, forgetting everything else to deal with this more serious matter. Smiling into the grave tawny eyes, she added calmly, "If you want me to know about it, then you'll tell me."

"Aren't you curious?"

"Of course I'm curious." Her voice was still calm. "I have the normal amount of female curiosity, after all. So just tell me one thing—does it have anything to do with us, or our future?"

"No," he said immediately.

"Then it isn't important, is it? Besides, I know you well enough to guess that you wouldn't get involved in a revolution except by accident or for a very good reason."

He hugged her. "Thank you, honey, for loving me and trusting me." His voice was a little uneven for a moment, then steadied as he went on. "I was sent to South America before the revolution began, to do some work for a U.S. company there. When the revolution started, I was . . . well, I was . . . requested . . . to stay for a while and keep an eye on things."

Reading between the lines—something she was very good at after a life with her father—Casey stared at him, pained. "Don't tell me. You're a dollar-a-year man for the government?"

He shrugged dismissingly. "Like you said—trouble-shooters travel a lot. Sometimes I was in a position to pick up useful information."

"I hope you're through with that sort of thing," she said uneasily. "I grew up surrounded by hush-hush goings-on, Storm, and I never liked it much."

The golden eyes gleamed with laughter. "What would they want with a settled, happily married Operations Co-ordinator with six kids?" he asked with laughter in his voice.

"Six?" Casey traced the line of his jaw with one finger, smiling at him. "I was thinking more along the lines of four, myself. There's the population explosion, you know."

"I don't think we should let that influence us," he said gravely.

"Will this house you're planning on hold six kids?" she asked cautiously.

"More than that. And we can always add on."

His hands were moving in a disturbing pattern over her back, and Casey tried to think straight. "Well, why don't we just start with one and work our way from there," she suggested, hearing the husky shiver in her voice.

With easy strength, he pulled her completely on top of him, his gaze fixed on her face. "I love you, princess," he said deeply, the honey-and-steel voice filled with utter certainty. "More than I'll ever be able to tell you."

"Never leave me," she whispered, letting her green eyes fill with all the love she had ever held inside herself. "I'd die if you left me."

"Leave you?" He drew her slowly forward until their lips were only a whisper apart. "You couldn't beat me off with a stick..."

* * *

It was a long time later when Casey stirred, feeling her husband's arms tighten around her and smiling with sleepy contentment. Her drowsy gaze fell on the bottle of champagne and two beribboned glasses on a table by the window, and she felt bound to mention it. "We haven't opened the champagne," she murmured.

With flattering disinterest, Storm muttered, "Who needs it?" and yawned.

Casey cuddled a little closer and suddenly the thought that had been floating nebulously in her mind for days came within reach. "If we have a girl," she said dreamily, "I want to name her Raine."

There was a moment of silence, and then Storm began to shake with silent laughter. "Don't tell me! Because—"

"Well, what else do you get from a storm . . . ?"

____ 06401-7 PRIMITIVE SPLENDOR #41 Katherine Swinford
____ 06424-6 GARDEN OF SILVERY DELIGHTS #42 Sharon Francis
____ 06521-8 STRANGE POSSESSION #43 Johanna Phillips
____ 06326-6 CRESCENDO #44 Melinda Harris
____ 05818-1 INTRIGUING LADY #45 Daphne Woodward
____ 06547-1 RUNAWAY LOVE #46 Jasmine Craig
____ 06423-8 BITTERSWEET REVENGE #47 Kelly Adams
____ 06541-2 STARBURST #48 Tess Ewing
____ 06540-4 FROM THE TORRID PAST #49 Ann Cristy
____ 06544-7 RECKLESS LONGING #50 Daisy Logan
____ 05851-3 LOVE'S MASQUERADE #51 Lillian Marsh
____ 06148-4 THE STEELE HEART #52 Jocelyn Day
____ 06422-X UNTAMED DESIRE #53 Beth Brookes
____ 06651-6 VENUS RISING #54 Michelle Roland
____ 06595-1 SWEET VICTORY #55 Jena Hunt
____ 06575-7 TOO NEAR THE SUN #56 Aimee Duvall
____ 05625-1 MOURNING BRIDE #57 Lucia Curzon
____ 06411-4 THE GOLDEN TOUCH #58 Robin James
____ 06596-X EMBRACED BY DESTINY #59 Simone Hadary
____ 06660-5 TORN ASUNDER #60 Ann Cristy
____ 06573-0 MIRAGE #61 Margie Michaels
____ 06650-8 ON WINGS OF MAGIC #62 Susanna Collins
____ 05816-5 DOUBLE DECEPTION #63 Amanda Troy
____ 06675-3 APOLLO'S DREAM #64 Claire Evans
____ 06680-X THE ROGUE'S LADY #69 Anne Devon
____ 06687-7 FORSAKING ALL OTHERS #76 LaVyrle Spencer
____ 06689-3 SWEETER THAN WINE #78 Jena Hunt
____ 06690-7 SAVAGE EDEN #79 Diane Crawford
____ 06691-5 STORMY REUNION #80 Jasmine Craig

All of the above titles are $175 per copy

Available at your local bookstore or return this form to:

SECOND CHANCE AT LOVE
Book Mailing Service, P.O. Box 690, Rockville Cntr., NY 11570

Please send me the titles checked above. I enclose _____.
Include 75¢ for postage and handling if one book is ordered; 50¢ per book for
two to five. If six or more are ordered, postage is free. California, Illinois, New
York and Tennessee residents please add sales tax.

NAME _____

ADDRESS _____

CITY_____ STATE ZIP_____

Allow six weeks for delivery.   SK-41

_____ 06692-3 THE WAYWARD WIDOW #81 Anne Mayfield
_____ 06693-1 TARNISHED RAINBOW #82 Jocelyn Day
_____ 06694-X STARLIT SEDUCTION #83 Anne Reed
_____ 06695-8 LOVER IN BLUE #84 Aimée Duvall
_____ 06696-6 THE FAMILIAR TOUCH #85 Lynn Lawrence
_____ 06697-4 TWILIGHT EMBRACE #86 Jennifer Rose
_____ 06698-2 QUEEN OF HEARTS #87 Lucia Curzon
_____ 06850-0 PASSION'S SONG #88 Johanna Phillips
_____ 06851-9 A MAN'S PERSUASION #89 Katherine Granger
_____ 06852-7 FORBIDDEN RAPTURE #90 Kate Nevins
_____ 06853-5 THIS WILD HEART #91 Margarett McKean
_____ 06854-3 SPLENDID SAVAGE #92 Zandra Colt
_____ 06855-1 THE EARL'S FANCY #93 Charlotte Hines
_____ 06858-6 BREATHLESS DAWN #94 Susanna Collins
_____ 06859-4 SWEET SURRENDER #95 Diana Mars
_____ 06860-8 GUARDED MOMENTS #96 Lynn Fairfax
_____ 06861-6 ECSTASY RECLAIMED #97 Brandy LaRue
_____ 06862-4 THE WIND'S EMBRACE #98 Melinda Harris
_____ 06863-2 THE FORGOTTEN BRIDE #99 Lillian Marsh
_____ 06864-0 A PROMISE TO CHERISH #100 LaVyrle Spencer
_____ 06865-9 GENTLE AWAKENING #101 Marianne Cole
_____ 06866-7 BELOVED STRANGER #102 Michelle Roland
_____ 06867-5 ENTHRALLED #103 Ann Cristy
_____ 06868-3 TRIAL BY FIRE #104 Faye Morgan
_____ 06869-1 DEFIANT MISTRESS #105 Anne Devon
_____ 06870-5 RELENTLESS DESIRE #106 Sandra Brown
_____ 06871-3 SCENES FROM THE HEART #107 Marie Charles
_____ 06872-1 SPRING FEVER #108 Simone Hadary
_____ 06873-X IN THE ARMS OF A STRANGER #109 Deborah Joyce
_____ 06874-8 TAKEN BY STORM #110 Kay Robbins
_____ 06899-3 THE ARDENT PROTECTOR #111 Amanda Kent

All of the above titles are $1.75 per copy

WHAT READERS SAY ABOUT
SECOND CHANCE AT LOVE BOOKS

"Your books are the greatest!"
   —*M. N., Carteret, New Jersey**

"I have been reading romance novels for quite some time, but the SECOND CHANCE AT LOVE books are the most enjoyable."
   —*P. R., Vicksburg, Mississippi**

"I enjoy SECOND CHANCE [AT LOVE] more than any books that I have read and I do read a lot."
   —*J. R., Gretna, Louisiana**

"I really think your books are exceptional . . . I read Harlequin and Silhouette and although I still like them, I'll buy your books over theirs. SECOND CHANCE [AT LOVE] is more interesting and holds your attention and imagination with a better story line . . ."
   —*J. W., Flagstaff, Arizona**

"I've read many romances, but yours take the 'cake'!"
   —*D. H., Bloomsburg, Pennsylvania**

"Have waited ten years for *good* romance books. Now I have them."
   —*M. P., Jacksonville, Florida**

*Names and addresses available upon request